Waiting for Princess Margaret

Also by EMMA TENNANT

FICTION

The Bad Sister
Hotel de Dream
Alice Fell
Woman, Beware Woman
Black Marina
Queen of Stones
Felony – A Private History of 'The Aspern Papers'
The House of Hospitalities
A Wedding of Cousins
Two Women of London
Faustine
Pemberley
Wild Nights

MEMOIRS

Strangers: A Family Romance
Girlitude
Burnt Diaries
A House in Corfu

Waiting for Princess Margaret

EMMA TENNANT

QUARTET BOOKS

First published in 2009 by
Quartet Books Limited
A member of the Namara Group
27 Goodge Street, London W1T 2LD

A catalogue record for this book
is available from the British Library

ISBN   978 0 7043 7183 5

Typeset by Antony Gray
Printed and bound in Great Britain by
T J International Ltd, Padstow, Cornwall

Contents

	Preface	7
	Prologue	9
One	Glen: A House and Its Head	15
Two	Glen	24
Three	Glen: A Fortune	32
Four	Glen: The Kennels	35
Five	Glen: The War	38
Six	Glen: Childhood	42
Seven	Glen: Alone	45
Eight	Glen: The Engagement	51
Nine	London, 2008	54
Ten	Glen, Summer 1954	57
Eleven	The Preparations	66
Twelve	The Narrow Escape	69
Thirteen	The Arrival	72
Fourteen	Summer 2002, Fulham	80
Fifteen	Mooning	85
Sixteen	The Clootie Horn	87
Seventeen	Great Aunts	90
Eighteen	'Wabster Charlie'	92

Nineteen	Cigarette Smoke	94
Twenty	The Pownie Goes to Edinburgh	97
Twenty-One	Down and Out	99
Twenty-Two	The Ball	105
Twenty-Three	Dancing Partners	109
Twenty-Four	Glen: Disappearances	113
Twenty-Five	The Search for Oliver Hope	114
Twenty-Six	Glen: Taking Leave	129
Twenty-Seven	Harcourts	134
Twenty-Eight	Glen: What Next?	142
Twenty-Nine	February 10th 2005	146
Thirty	October 18th 2007	150
Epilogue	March 2007	152

Preface

Waiting for Princess Margaret is part fact, part fiction, dictated by the memory of a childhood and adolescence over-hung by unexplained relations and twisted family roots. I had intended to write a novel, but the conventions were too restricting; and I knew the characters portrayed here had no need of false names or invented addresses, Indeed, a leading character in the book is Glen, a house in the Borders of Scotland – a place which has proved both a lure and a curse to many members of the family.

The fuzzy relationship between fact, fiction and memory provides the atmosphere of *Waiting for Princess Margaret*, a book belonging in all three categories. Based on fact, with the narrator's voice embedded with the voices of others; imagined as a work of fiction and inspired by memory, it is as near, for me at least, as it's possible to get to reality.

Prologue

'There's a new secret,' the pale-faced young man sitting on the floor opposite me says. 'I had to tell you. It's about Glen.'

'But – ' I begin. The floor is covered with festive wrapping paper and rolls of Sellotape. I start snipping with a pair of scissors so the smallest present, a tiny bottle of the iris-root scent my mother loves, will end up looking as if I've taken some trouble with it. 'I don't understand,' I think of saying – but a sense of dread, a kind of stubbornness gets in the way. I don't understand – of course I don't – but I certainly don't want to. In this family there are plenty of secrets – and unwanted revelations – and sheer bad-news items that strangers like to share with us: please don't tell me. It's Christmas next week, for God's sake!

As I stare mutinously across at him, I feel guilt at not wanting to hear what may be the latest fantasy of a youthful relative diagnosed six months ago with cancer and given less than half that to live. Surely I should play along with whatever his fairy story may turn out to be and pretend I'm as excited as he obviously is: the pale face has reddened in the effort to convince me of the truth of the news about the house where I once spent the happiest and the saddest days of my life. I know Henry has been off the radar for some

9

years now and seems unlikely to find himself before it's too late. Do I even have to listen to him, let alone believe the inevitable tales of disinheritance and foiled expectations which make up the lure – and the curse – of Glen?

Henry shifts uncomfortably on the hard cord carpet where he sits (so as, I realise with a sinking heart, to seem near to me) as he recounts the latest news. He has joined in doing up presents for other members of the family in a spirit of togetherness. It's time to say something, to ask for details, but I still can't, so I'm the one to move nearer to him – to show, I suppose, that I'm not shocked or disgusted by the bombshell he is obviously proud of dropping on an unplanned visit to my flat in West London.

'All right – tell me,' I say – for now all I can sense is that reassurance, affection, are really what are needed by this tragic figure who sees himself as the puller-together of the family and can find the courage to call on me, his father's half-sister, who must seem to him to be a distant member of a long-split family. 'I'll come and see you – I'll come whenever you want me to.' (I mean to St Mary's, a hospital Henry has been in and out of many times, but to which my own visits have been shamefully perfunctory.) 'Of course I'll come, it doesn't matter what's happened at Glen.' Yet even saying the name of the house makes me go as blank as a dementia sufferer – except a dementia sufferer talks and forgets at the same time. I can never forget.

The superficiality of my remarks sink in, and I must have cringed even more than Henry, the tall nephew with pale orange hair and long legs and a laugh that makes him likeable as soon as you hear it, did, because words now come to him with a new intensity. 'Bella. She's got proof she's who she says she is and she's going to take over Glen.' Possibly my reaction to his assertion of a new claim from a distant relation (as I'd thought Bella to be) has fired him up further: he will now give me details, which I both dread and know I have to have. 'The European courts,' Henry says, because of course he has been expecting me to demand the full facts. 'Your father considered himself to be heir to Glen and all the rest – but Bella comes from a line that was ignored because it's female – even though it's older. Strasbourg has changed all that. Bella is confident she's going to win.'

'I see,' I interrupt him, and find I'm speaking in a sensible voice, the kind of voice grown-ups put on when they find themselves in a tricky situation with a child. 'So we all do what Bella says in future, then.' I realise at this point that I am almost believing his far-fetched story, so great is Henry's desire to convince me of its truth.

This isn't the moment, though, to make reproaches or show doubt. A sudden premonition has grabbed me – it feels as if a hand, cold as ice, is holding me in its grip, so I can't look across at Henry's beaming, conspiratorial face – and I know that I am about to become as certain as he of the truth of the assertion that I dismissed earlier as make-believe.

'No, it's nearer than that. Your father,' Henry says as I discard the pretence of wrapping identical scarves and woollen hats for my daughters and stare back at him. 'Your father gave Bella an assurance that she would inherit Glen.' He laughs as he repeats the nickname, bestowed by me on my father years ago but never known or heard by him: 'Kit.

Kit gave her power of attorney and all that. And then there are the European courts . . . '

Now, as if I've known for ages that this was coming, Henry can concentrate on other things, his secret out in the open. He rises, and slings an exotic-looking bag round his neck before walking to the door. Over his head, a primitive water tank gurgles high on the wall, a feature we tried to incorporate into the flat and then gave up on, knowing we needed all the space we could get for ourselves and couldn't make money from letting it.

'Where are you going for Christmas?' I hear myself call out. Somehow this new 'secret', like anything to do with Glen's possible future or fought-over past, means I haven't found the strength to rise to my feet and end the visit with polite goodbyes. I know the answer already, of course: a picture of snow and a dark hall, where a festive tree with real candles comes to mind with the obedience of cliché.

'Oh, Glen,' replies Henry as he goes on his too-long legs to the front door. 'I'll see you when I get back.' He turns and crosses the room with two strides. A soft, papery kiss lands on my cheek, then he turns again and this time the front door closes quietly behind him. I imagine him for a minute, too tall for the sleeper in the train rushing north; the yellow-and-white-chequered cotton sheet that I supply from memories of night-time journeys with my younger brother to Galashiels and then to Glen is too short to cover this emaciated giant. He turns restlessly, pale ginger hair twisted on the decorative bag he has made into a pillow – then, as the train plunges into a tunnel, the picture goes and he has disappeared.

*   *   *

'Did dad have an affair?' My mother is speaking: I have rung to tell her of Henry's visit this afternoon. It's a relief to hear her voice: my mother is always calm, despite the frequent surprises, shocks and hatreds revealed in the family: now, she doesn't sound convinced or even particularly interested by the news brought to me today.

'Oh, I don't think so,' I say into the receiver, as a picture of the distant branch that is Bella's connection with us comes into my mind. (I'm beginning to learn that the concept is hard to take in, perhaps because it summons up the unacceptable: the sex life of a parent or husband. 'An affair', with its *Brief Encounter* connotations, is easier to go along with.)

'Can it be true?' my mother wonders, all the way from her house in Greece. I can almost hear the Ionian Sea washing Henry's absurd claim on to the rocks around the bay where she lives.

I tell her – lamely, I confess – that it seemed true enough. 'Bella – she's going to have Glen and' – I try to make a joke of it – 'she'll put gold taps in the bathrooms,' as if this could make a difference to my mother's reaction to my unexpected piece of news – and it doesn't, as her silence shows.

'I wish you were coming for Christmas,' my mother says finally. Just as I realise she wants me to ring off as badly as I do, she adds, 'Are Colin and the children going up to Glen this year?'

'Oh yes, I think so,' I say, while trying to banish the picture I have implanted in my mother's mind and my own: the impossible picture of my father with a new baby. Bella, who we'd all been told was something like an eighth cousin, taken in when first her mother and then her father died.

'There's going to be snow in Scotland,' my mother says, and her voice brightens as she summons this symbol of purity. 'Darling, ring again soon,' she ends – and I know she means it, though she'd prefer not to hear the kind of thing I have just forced her to listen to.

On a note of happy botanical enthusiasm we discuss the appearance of wild cyclamen on the hills of Corfu. I say that we've had the last of the conkers.

Just as the horse chestnut guards its brown, polished fruit in a carapace that is painful to the touch, green and prickly, yielding its treasure only at bursting point, so my mother's natural reserve shields and protects her inner beliefs and thoughts. The Bella-at-Glen information will never be referred to again – and if the subject comes up, it will elicit the same gentle, disbelieving response as before.

CHAPTER ONE

Glen: A House and Its Head

OCTOBER 4TH 1984

It's my father's funeral and a small convoy of sleek black cars blocks the narrow gateway to the kirk at Traquair in Peeblesshire, deep in James Hogg country and just a mile and a half above the valley that leads to Glen. The overall impression is of brightness, not gloom: my mother has decreed that a wreath of gentians should descend into the grave with my father's ashes, and the scarlet and yellow leaves on the trees surrounding this most romantic and lovely of places lend an air of carnival, rather than grief, to the scene. There are few mourners – everyone knows my father's happiest years were in another, very different valley on the west coast of Corfu, where he painted, sat ruminatively on the terrace and generally enjoyed the shifting of responsibility for the upkeep and future of Glen from his shoulders to those of his eldest son. The fact that Glen was made over to Colin in 1963 before our father sold the family business and emigrated to Greece in 1965 makes his burial here twenty years later seem strange. But my mother, his second wife and fifteen years younger, has doubtless gone along with the instructions in her husband's will. Christopher will be buried where his family is buried. He was a Tennant

15

and he will join the other Tennants, as near as possible to Glen.

The rituals of a Scottish funeral had been unknown to me, and as we enter the kirk I whisper to my younger sister that last night I read up on them and learned that it is perfectly legal to conduct a funeral in the open air in Scotland: in the eighteenth and nineteenth centuries it was the norm. Wouldn't it be beautiful to do that here today? Of course, it's too late, and the requests of a female member of the family don't count for much either: a distant cousin, one-time managing director of C. Tennant Sons & Co., puts me in my place as he whistles past, waving his arms to my mother and sister, signalling that my father's widow should push ahead of the straggling band of mourners by the door of the kirk and sit in the front row of chairs inside. 'Do go where you like,' Julian says to me as he rushes past again – he is Julian Tennant, black-haired, with a booming voice everyone can hear – and I realise I've disgraced myself at my father's funeral by asking for the impossible, as I some-how knew I would.

Colin is already in the front row on the right-hand side. He is smartly if slightly oddly dressed: one always seeks out the unexpected detail – no pockets, in one long-ago suit of which he was particularly proud, or a fabric with all the artificiality of a circus outfit, shiny and gleaming. Colin's wife is sitting beside him. She is in a black coat and skirt, expensive-looking and by far the most conventional in the congregation as I look around to check on the others. She is also properly made-up and looks pretty, which is more than can be said for my sister (mac) or me (shabby overcoat); my

16

other sister-in-law's down-to-earth country clothes show that she has a practical attitude to fashion.

The service is short (it turns out, after all, that a good proportion of it takes place out in the burial ground) and the whole way through it I wonder how Colin can be going to react to it. He's looked sideways once and seen my mother, my sister and me; he has turned farther and seen the family members who came up with us on the flight to Edinburgh and shared our kedgeree at a hotel before taking the hired car out to Traquair; and now he is listening to the minister's address.

'From all I have heard . . . ' come the strong Scottish tones of a man who was not here at the time of my father's stewardship of Glen and had no knowledge of my father's religious beliefs. He took me regularly from Glen to Traquair in a pushchair to sit through the Sabbath sermon at this kirk; I must have been under three years old and can remember nothing of what took place here. 'From what I have heard,' the minister insists, as I sit in a furnace of embarrassment on a chair beside my mother, 'those were the golden years. For all those employed as farm workers at Glen House, and their families, it was a golden age.'

Colin's head, long and pointed if seen from the back, shows no reaction to what sounds like a deliberate chastisement from the pulpit. The dome, hairless but finely shaped, is what used to be known in the Edwardian age to which its owner seems strangely to belong (Colin likes to describe himself as 'an eccentric') as 'distinguished'. Usually, a straw hat covers it – but today, at his father's funeral, he hasn't gone so far as to sport this reminder of his life on Mustique,

17

his island in the Caribbean, which is written about in the *Daily Mail* with hideous regularity. He is, quite simply, the heir, who inherited Glen when our father went to live in Greece two decades earlier and had only one thing left to complete his legacy: the much-scorned title.

'Anne [his wife] doesn't want to be Lady Glenconner,' I'd heard he'd said in London. (She is an earl's daughter and to be addressed as the spouse of 'the third Baron Glenconner' was hardly an enticement.) 'But Princess Margaret says we must.' And so, of course they did.

What did Colin think of this snub from the minister of Traquair kirk? The obvious implication, that he had cared little for his work force, preferring rum punches and visiting royalty to running a farm – on taking possession of the place he announced proudly that 'the cows have been driven away in a van' – might matter little to him, though it would account for the sparsely attended funeral, the labourers on the estate presumably having gone years ago to seek employment elsewhere. It was impossible to know what the new laird made of this surprisingly blunt sermon. Nor did I dare look round in any direction, for fear of seeing triumph on the faces of those who agreed fervently with the minister and had possibly supplied the information that my father's management of the land at Glen was incomparably superior to that of his son. Those who felt friendship for Colin – and my mother must be counted as one: a stepmother at the age of twenty-one to an eight-year-old boy bewildered by the change in his family circumstances, she had never been anything other than thoughtful and considerate in her dealings with him – would surely be pleased if someone came forward later to set the record straight as far as possible.

That some of the members of the congregation gathered to bid farewell to my father had different ideas of what was actually going to happen later only became evident when we had all filed out into the October sunlight and walked up the grassy slope punctuated by gravestones and overlooking the landscape I knew so well from my childhood: Orchard Mains Farm at the foot of the brae; the winding lane that led to Glen Lodge, the hills still purple with heather; the clumps of silver birches, where red and white mushrooms too frighteningly poisonous to pick grew under the trees. A strong wind began blowing as the minister, now standing at the graveside, offered his last address. As the leaves on the trees across the valley formed a tapestry of brightly waving flags, I gripped my mother and sister each by the hand. We could have been ready for battle, facing an encroaching army on the far side of the valley.

It was as my mother's wreath of gentians tumbled down into the darkness that I realised something was happening by the gate into the cemetery. A woman was screaming – for a while the noise must have been muffled, perhaps by the positioning of the hearse and the other black limos, which were now turning into the road beyond the kirk, ready for the off – and as she screamed other voices were raised, those of a man and of a woman with a strong, low voice. My mother, watching the undertakers as they walked down the steep ground, and my sister, her eyes still filled with sadness, seemed to pay no heed to the commotion; drawn down past the black-suited professional mourners, each apparently more consumed by grief than the last, I stumbled over grassy hillocks and found myself by the back door into the kirk. There I could not see but could certainly hear what was going on at the white gate, which opened on to the road to St Mary's Loch, the hills beyond and the River Yarrow. And it was of this land, haunted by border ballads, running with the blood of Red and Black Douglases, divided by the river as it curved along the valley of Blackhouse, that Colin's wife shrieked as she struggled to end a feud that had gone on for years between my elder half-brother and other members of the family: the feud over the ownership of a part of the Glen estate, Blackhouse.

'Shake hands,' my sister-in-law repeated, her voice jagged now with weeping and screaming. 'Go on . . . Shake hands!'

I didn't wait to discover if her plea was answered. I knew it would make little difference if it was. The lure and curse of Glen had surfaced again, at the time that my father's ashes were being placed in the ground.

*   *   *

We drove back to Edinburgh and waited for the plane to return us to London. Some of the cousins who had flown up with us gathered to sit huddled in our small gathering of immediate family as they had been on the journey north, but it was clear that my mother had no strength left in her to smile at them or talk; with her sister Anne by her side, her face was closed and her expression distant. Possibly she saw, as I did, the trajectory of the guests at Glen as they arrived for a wake to which we had – or had not? I never discovered – been invited. In her mind, she may have stepped into the house where she had lived – not all the time; the war took both my parents to Turkey and my father to Cairo – enough of the time to feel it was a family home, and she was probably wondering, as I was, why we weren't there to drink and socialise as was the custom, particularly in Scotland.

Looking over at my aunt, a committed Socialist with a kind heart and a strong desire to help my mother, who had been alone with my father in his last hours in Greece, I see the sisters in the dining-room at Glen. I have walked in my imagining across the chilly hall with the grass-green carpet that must have come as a real shock to old retainers, neighbours and the like, as must the white walls introduced by the laird's new wife. 'There was dark panelling everywhere,' my mother said when I asked her to describe her reaction to the mock-baronial castle, which she first saw when brought north by my father after their marriage in a register office in London. 'I felt guilty when they burned it in the stables; it smouldered there for days.'

As I try to order my thoughts, I am looking at my mother and aunt, and they show themselves to me ensconced in the Glen dining-room, with its long mahogany table, which is laid for tea, with plates of drop scones, biscuits and various cakes. There are other people round the table: my grandfather, for one, who is invited each year by his daughter, my mother; my Aunt Clare (my father's sister, whose snobbery empties the room on most occasions, my grandfather being a prime target for her disdain); and my other half-brother James, younger by two years than Colin. It is he who brings the family's sense of its importance to the fore whenever possible: from the Tennants as yeoman farmers in eighteenth-century

Ayrshire, to the Tennants as makers of a chemical fortune in Glasgow a century later, and thence to Sir Charles Tennant whose portrait hangs in the Old Drawing-Room: tiny, with a pointy beard and eyes that could spot a goldmine from the far side of the world.

My grandfather George, who has no such antecedents, chuckles sycophantically when James goes off into his account of Tennant achievements and companies – and not for the first time today I make an effort to banish the picture I have summoned up from my mind. I do this by holding my gaze on my mother and aunt: how different they are from the Tennants, I think, how modest despite having an interesting family history of their own. Quakers and Catholics, clever and devoted to good works, my mother's family is the antithesis of my father's. Yet, silenced by James's intolerable boasting, they fade out of the scene altogether: like moths drawn to a candle flame and unable to extricate themselves from the nightmarish family meal in which I have cruelly placed them, they are subsumed and cannot cut free from the family my mother married into.

I blush and take my gaze away from these intelligent, subtle women. I am nothing to do with the high-coloured, money-obsessed life which generations of Tennants have been proud to lead. My life is different, I tell myself. Then I think of the screaming in Traquair graveyard and I see Colin, jaunty in a silk suit, straw hat adding a Garbo-esque touch to his regular (and apparently ageless) features. He's standing in the doorway at Glen and smiling for the photographer the *Mail* will undoubtedly have sent there.

One of the cousins gets up and goes off uncertainly in

22

search of the gents. By the time he's back our flight is called. And by the time I'm in my seat next to my aunt I'm halfway – or so I believe – to recovery. The sense of sanity she and my mother give off is as strong and bracing as fresh air after a storm. But Anne, married to and now separated from the philosopher Richard Wollheim, sometimes fails to see how much I appreciate her distance from the Tennants. She is only trying to please me, I know, when she leans across to speak to my mother. 'Lizzy, what do you think? I've just been saying to Emma that she was Christopher's favourite. Don't you agree? And after Emma, Colin. Don't you think?'

CHAPTER TWO

Glen

When my mother married a week after her twenty-first birthday in March 1935, she could hardly have expected, just four and a half years later, to find her husband's first wife preparing to ensconce herself and her two sons in the home from which divorce had banished her, along with hopes of any reconciliation. Nor would my mother have dreamt that this scenario, chillingly reminiscent of Daphne du Maurier's classic *Rebecca*, could even be contemplated, let alone implemented by her husband – and, unwillingly, herself. Of course, war had broken out. Colin and James must be safe, far from the bombs. An infant half-sister – that is, me – was already there, holding the fort as only a small child can do, Nanny (who had been nanny to my mother and her sister Anne) was fully on the qui vive for attempts at running away or stoking up the coals on the open fire in the nursery in order to start a blaze. Colin, who was entering his teens at the time of this further disruption in his life, would keep an eye on the house he would one day inherit. Pamela, his mother, for reasons of tact in the presence of a new wife only eight years older than her stepson, was seldom mentioned when it became clear that this was the most sensible way of safeguarding the lives of all three of my father's children: if the boys' mother had to be included, then she would rank lower than Nanny in my father's eyes.

24

My mother and I are sitting in my younger brother's flat in London. She stays here when she comes over from Greece and I want to ask her questions I've never asked before. I've told her I'm looking at the possible reasons for the evil times that have fallen on the family – and as always, as she gazes at me apprehensively, I reassure her that none of the battles, the anguish or the blame lie with her. It's more that Glen – I inevitably put it all down to Glen – has produced divisions in the family. Why didn't we go to my father's wake, for example, when my mother has always shown affection for Colin even if it was impossible to feel any fondness for James? (Why? I don't know: his arrogance perhaps, his assumption that people would want to hear his litany of boring facts, gleaned from an encyclopaedia.) Perhaps the reason was that Colin had waited too long to come into the place he has never liked: the show-off château built by Sir Charles in the mid nineteenth century in order to impress Mr Gladstone and the rest. But then, Colin is a show-off himself, in spades you could say, from his attention-grabbing suits to his parties and balls. One of the most outstanding of these was the Wrecking Party at Whistler's house in Chelsea, bought by Colin and destroyed so he could build a new ultra-modern extravaganza. Why does he hate Glen so much? And why, when he buys and sells houses all the time, hasn't he sold it, when the entail has ended with him and he is free to dispose of it all if he wishes?

'I don't know,' my mother says. And I surmise from the ensuing silence that she and I are thinking the same thought: Glen may have impressed Mr Gladstone – and hosted Sir Charles's son-in-law, Prime Minister Asquith's house parties – but it didn't impress anyone important now. Even the Royal Family's Balmoral, the nearest in style to Glen, was an obvious joke, visitable only in summer months when there were plenty of animals to kill. And Glen, after a succession of bad grouse-shooting seasons on the moors, had plenty of nothing to offer, in Colin's view at least. Culturally, the place was also a disaster: in the 1950s and 1960s, when he took over the running of the place, Victorian piles were mocked or excoriated. His first act of ownership was to cover over the plasterwork foliage on the bedroom and dining-room ceilings. Shortly after a visit from an art connoisseur who came from London on a Scottish tour (the eighteenth-century mansions, such as Marchmont and Mellerstain, were architecturally 'good'; Glen was bad), nearly all of Sir Charles's collection of English portraits and landscapes was sold. The Cotmans and the Boningtons and the Joshua Reynoldses and the Turners were replaced by huge and hideous pictures of subjects such as our grandfather Edward Tennant fishing on Loch Eddy, the artificial stretch of water named after him, at the end of the valley that was Glen.

'It was tricky,' my mother says when I ask, still in pursuit of the cause of Colin's dissatisfaction with Glen, despite the glowing descriptions in Margot Asquith's diary of the 'most beautiful place on earth' and the obvious fact that every single member of the family except himself had fallen under the spell of Glen. The heather that came right down to terraced gardens, the magic Fethan Wood, setting for Hogg's tales of the supernatural – it even had a fairy ring of its own, complete with toadstools and moss of a vicious emerald

green – were irresistible to everyone except Colin. The road
leading from the house built by Sir Charles in 1856 meanders
through soft foxglove country and comes to an abrupt end
two and a half miles later at the boathouse and the black
waters of the loch. How could anyone fortunate enough to
own this dream of loveliness feel so little for it? Or was I,
the only child to have lived at Glen full-time (the war was
responsible and I'm guiltily grateful), the most appreciative
of its charms? I hated London when the war ended and I
was brought south to go to school: was I doomed to live ever
after in my memories of the place, as Margot confided to
her diary she did, incontestable owner in her imagination of
the place where she had spent her childhood? But at least, I
answered my own question, when he was owner of Glen,
Margot's brother had liked her to visit when she pleased;
and my father (I remember him sitting at table in the
dining-room when news was brought that Lady Oxford was
here; she would go straight up to the loch, there was no
need to greet her) had made no objections to these surprise
visits by one who suffered an obsession with Glen. Not my
elder half-brother though – and I must have sighed, lost, as
happened so often, in my sense of regret at being cut off
from the place I still thought of as home.

'You mean where she was going to sleep and that kind of
thing?' I say. Reverting to Colin's own childhood and the
sense of displacement he must have felt at his mother's new
status at Glen since the divorce seems the only way to
examine the problem. And yes, it must have been tricky. I
agree with my mother when she adds, 'You wouldn't have
liked it much.'

'But didn't you feel you might never get back?' I say, because I know that my mother went with my father on his mission to Turkey in 1940. 'Wasn't that what was most frightening?'

'Europe closed behind us,' my mother says. And I do think for the first time that this must certainly have been terrifying for a mother who had left her only child behind and saw no prospect of finding me until, if ever, the war ended. Throw into the pot that the two-year-old was to all intents and purposes alone in a castle (Nanny was there; Pamela and the boys had not yet come) and a Gothic horror movie reveals itself.

'When we were finally able to get back,' my mother says, 'it took three months.' She has forgotten her fear of a usurper in her home in Scotland, and relives the long trek from Turkey through Syria, zigzagging down to Palestine and on to Cairo, then a final plane to the Cape followed by a long wait for a troop carrier to bring them across a torpedo-ridden sea to Liverpool. Perhaps Margot was right, I think: you are the owner of the places you visit in memory: no one can take them away or alter them for you. But my mother is also good at blocking out those scenes she would rather not revisit, and she gives me a puzzled look when I press her for further details of her life at Glen after they returned – she seriously ill by then with a kidney condition.

How did her married life begin, before war came and interrupted everyone's lives? All I have heard from her is that 'Maud Russell, a friend' had invited both my father and herself to Mottisfont: now I want to know more. There is only one photograph of the wedding – or rather, of the minutes after the wedding, of my father and mother as they make what appears to be a rushed escape through a crowd at Caxton Hall, the London register office where my mother became the Baroness Glenconner. I've heard that she scratched off the large initial 'G' and (more embarrassing still) the Tennant family crest from the expensive luggage her mother had given her. In the photograph, the tall dark young woman who walks at my father's speed across the hall looks as shy as I've ever seen her: was the day so painful for her? Surely there was something to look forward to – didn't they go somewhere (I wouldn't say the word honeymoon) for a short holiday?

'We went to have lunch with my parents,' my mother says. 'And then we went straight up to Glen.'

'On the train?' I see the journeys I made for years, between the grimness of St Pancras and the hills and moors and burns that showed you were coming to the Border country, to Galashiels.

'It was March but none of the daffodils were out,' my mother remembers: it becomes clear that she'd had no idea of how capable Glen was of hanging on to winter until the bitter end. 'Elizabeth has gone to Scotland with her baron,' one of my mother's old friends, the spy Donald Maclean, joked at the time. The romance had clearly baffled my mother's generation of Upper Bohemians, as they would be known today: habitués of the Gargoyle, a favourite nightclub owned by my father's brother David, the girls (like my mother) frequently students at the Slade.

'It can't have been your first visit to Glen?' I say – but I know somehow that it was. Vulgarly, drawn into the picture of the second Mrs de Winter as she arrives at Manderley, I go on and ask how many servants were waiting there, on the steps below the high doors and mock Gothic stone battlements. 'Oh, just old Mrs McKay,' replies my mother. Then, guilty of upsetting the memory of an old woman who had looked after my mother and father in their first days together, 'I'm afraid she wasn't a very good cook.'

Glen, with all the dark panelling intact (deer's antlers on the side, portraits of dead animals in the front hall) must have been a challenge to my mother on that first visit. She must also have sensed the ambivalence of her new husband's feelings about the place. Unlike his grandfather Sir Charles, who had made Glen a show-place of the fame and fortune he had enjoyed all his life, and unlike my father's father Eddy, who had dedicated himself to shooting and fishing and recorded his successes in vellum-bound volumes, my father had had to live in the shadow of another house and quite a different landscape, those loved by his mother in the South of England at Wilsford. It was never possible to tell, I concluded when I was older and watched him walk around Glen from one large cold room to another, whether he was fond of the house and surrounding hills and fields or whether they represented an intolerable burden. The house, unheated and unheatable in those days, provided a faint echo of an Edwardian past, when dependants and descendants came to shoot or fish for trout in the loch: the absence of the army of servants such establishments need made caring for guests extremely difficult. Most of the land, too, was moor: it was all very picturesque, but this was a House that gave its Head a hard time. My father, who had a fine sense of humour, was seldom smiling when he preceded the factor out of the library after a meeting.

Perhaps, I wondered when trying to examine the reasons for his silences and abstracted manner, these difficulties were the cause of his decision never to think or talk about the past, of my mother's fervent reserve and of his strong dislike of any mention of human feelings. ('I won't have any son of mine being psychological,' he said on the occasion of Colin's outburst on a drive up from London to Edinburgh when in his early twenties.) Music was also not welcome in any part of Glen. The grand piano in the drawing-room sat untouched, only opened when Colin came to Glen and sat playing from a book of old songs. 'I am so dreadfully mis-understood / So lady be good to me' would bring me down from my chilly bedroom – but my father entering the room would, if asked why music was anathema to him, reply that he found it 'sentimental'. No one ever dared to ask where this dread of sentimentality had come from, or even what it comprised. But refusing to take the hint, Colin played on.

In the light of the address made by the minister at Traquair kirk on the occasion of our father's funeral, it's possible to understand what Colin must have felt on hearing the compliments apparently paid by a misty-eyed workforce to the previous laird of Glen. Appointed the new laird in the mid 1960s, Colin had developed his 'eccentricity' for twenty years now. As time passed, he would hike it up, even going to the extent of standing for Parliament and hosting 'Scottish-themed' balls at Glen for the SNP.

CHAPTER THREE

Glen: A Fortune

Where you from? Where you from?
Won'cha tell me 'fore I'm gone?
'Cos if I don't leave now, I won't be goin' nowhere.

NEW ORLEANS JAZZ SONG

The element that moved the Tennants from a hut with requisite hole in the roof to let out smoke from the fire to the flag-flying imitation castle in the Borders was chlorine liquor, for which Charles Tennant, friend of Robert Burns, radical and inventor, obtained a patent in 1795. Refusing a knighthood, on the side of Napoleon and of Queen Caroline, from his St Rollox factory in Glasgow Charles founded a huge chemical empire which needed only the speculative genius of his grandson (later Sir) Charles to grow global. Scientific brilliance, mining and metallurgical interests, railways and bleach brought an ever-increasing fortune all the way through the nineteenth century. And when the century ended – or in fact six years into the twentieth – Sir Charles died aged eighty-one. At eight years old, he had carried a banner for the Reform Bill of 1832. At his death in Biarritz he was mourned by King Edward VII.

Snobbery, a strong family trait that was at its most noticeable in the late Bart's grandchildren, was embraced

enthusiastically by a family still laughed at for its pre-
tensions and its fortune. Clare, daughter of Sir Charles's
son Eddy, brought a particularly virulent form of snobbery
to all she knew of her victims' lives. Colin, grandson of
Eddy, the hapless husband of Pamela, one of Sargent's
Wyndham Sisters, took a leaf from her book. No one –
except of course a duke or a French aristocrat – could escape
his or Aunt Clare's witticisms and sharp, mocking eye.

'Oh yes, the French relations,' my mother says when I
point out that Colin's mother was not in the least snobbish
herself, despite having apparently provided her son with
Bourbon ancestors, along with comtes and comtesses, some
of these confusingly bearing English names pronounced in
the French manner – 'Balfoor', my mother remembers, and
'Harcoor'. But at this name she falls silent, and I sense a
family mystery. 'No,' my mother says when I press her.
'Nothing.'

Surrounded by reference books and various editions of
the *Almanac de Gotha*, the title-hunter's bible, Colin filled
his lonely and infrequent visits to Glen as a young man
with the dreams and longings produced by visions of royal
ancestry. The 'Balfoors' and the 'Harcoors' were before
long joined by an impeccable noblewoman from the far side
of the Channel: her name, if I'm remembering correctly,
was Brenda de Bourbon Bussy – but whether this was an
invention fit for a romantic novel or a real person never
became clear. (Certainly this fantasy figure was never to be
invited to Glen: it was hard to imagine my father's reaction
if she had come; he would probably have kept his perfect
manners and waited quietly for the visit to be over.) The

Balfoors and Harcoors, equally disappointingly, appeared to
be too grand to suffer the experience of coming to Scotland –
to our house, anyway.

'No, Glen wasn't fashionable,' my mother agrees when we
return to the early years, with Pamela moving apprehensively
into her former home and my mother just as fearfully stuck
by the Bosporus with my father and his wartime negotiations
with the Turks. 'Until, of course, Princess Margaret – if that
did make it fashionable,' she adds uncertainly. Her voice
betrays her loathing of the world her sister-in-law Clare came
to love and personify, that world of society usually described
as brittle and shallow – and rightly so, though it's possible to
understand, for an isolated, confused young man such as
Colin, that it did at least bring the promise of fun. For one
with little or no interest in the Glen farm – or for shooting
game, unless each butt held a titled shot within its heathery
confines – life without these connections and fantasies would
have been bleak.

CHAPTER FOUR

Glen: The Kennels

When war broke out, my parents were in the South of France. 'A hotel in Cannes,' says my mother, but she can't remember its name.

'A grand hotel?' I ask, knowing that Aunt Clare, the least favourite of the relatives she had taken on at the time of her marriage to my father, had been the third in the party.

'Oh, probably not grand enough,' my mother replies – but I see she no longer has any interest in the name of the hotel; she's breathing in her best-loved smells and memories: a field of lavender; thick honey in its cardboard container with Alpes Maritimes printed on it in tall letters; red wine as old Monsieur Voisin made it. There was a small vineyard next to the ruined farmhouse my father had bought a couple of years before and intended to repair so that he and my mother could escape Glen and go south to the sun. Olive groves formed a boundary round the place and narcissi grew under the trees in spring. 'So many cars trying to get to Boulogne,' my mother says. 'Terrible traffic jams.' And she closes her eyes, as if September 3rd 1939 has overtaken the modest paradise of the house, La Baumette, where she and my father would, when the war was over, paint the rooms and sit under the palm on a terrace with a mosaic of pebbles taken from the beach.

'She must have been annoyed when war was declared?' I pressed my mother – I enjoyed teasing her about Clare, who could always be counted on to do the exact opposite of what my mother did in any circumstances. 'I suppose she went looking for the Duchess of Windsor,' I guessed. 'I mean, they were all down there when war broke out, weren't they?'

My mother said there was one person my father insisted on going to see before joining the great exodus north to Boulogne. She appears in his brief memoir of the war – but, with characteristic reticence, he never made any reference to her in the near half-century between the end of the war and his death. She was Maxine Eliot, the Queen of the Riviera, said to be the lover of Winston Churchill, who came to paint the sea and the pines and olive trees. All the South of France's smart set was there, Somerset Maugham and the rest, and the Windsors and their hangers-on; I couldn't help thinking they were just the kind of people my mother would have hated to spend time with. When after the declaration of war the rush to get to England was under way, wasn't it rather odd that my father went off alone to the villa on the coast, to say goodbye to his old friend Maxine?

'Oh I don't know,' says my mother. 'Yes, that was its name: the Château l'Horizon!' And having remembered the name, she searches further for her own memories of the place. My father's brief memoir states that Maxine Eliot had been kind to him. My mother recalls most of all that the villa had a chute, straight down into the sea. And I catch her smiling as in her mind she rushes down in one whoosh! into the depths of the Mediterranean.

'But what about me?' I said, and even as I did so I found myself ashamed: I could have been two years old, as I was when England and Germany went to war, my parents caught in the panic. Isn't what I'm doing – or attempting, at least – a kind of reconstruction of members of the family and their past lives? 'What about me' isn't the point, or shouldn't be. But my mother takes my question seriously and thinks hard before answering.

'You went to The Kennels,' my mother says.

CHAPTER FIVE

Glen: The War

Working out my mother's friendships, not my father's: it seemed when I looked much later for his old pals that those who still lived had been part of work, like Novomesky, who drove my parents to Palestine from Syria in their great escape in the spring of 1941 from Turkey, or distant relatives, like the Spanish-featured Michael Tennant, who lived up in the north of Scotland near Cawdor Castle, by the edge of a loch that was black all the year round. My father didn't enjoy chatting, the word used by upper-class women to describe a satisfying (and usually malicious) way of passing the time; my mother never employed the term. He liked to discuss the very distant past: discoveries of Neanderthals and their immediate successors proved to be a good topic; and Outer Space, where he dreamed of planets and previously unknown stars visible (in black and white) in the new astronomy books. At a time when the old houses were crumbling under the burden of taxation and war (Glen was not a heritage number ripe for rescue, and was, he assured us, impossible to maintain) he chose to concentrate on the dinosaurs and the mysteries of the universe. Threats that a) Glen would have to go under the hammer and b) he would have to move into the factor's house (if the estate was sold, it was hard to see how we could do this) alternated in the freezing dining-room. My father would not stoop to eating in the pantry, where the house's only warming cupboard helped the chilblains from which we all suffered. The staff had one by one, with the exception of Tibbie from the lodge at the end of the drive, been swallowed up by the war. To leave Nanny alone in charge would have been risky – there was always the gamekeeper's house on the back road to Glen, The Kennels.

*   *   *

What is the name for one's father's first wife – for the child of a subsequent marriage to refer to her by, that is? She can't be a stepmother and shouldn't be confused with the real mother – although I have a mental picture of myself, when my parents were away on their interminable travels in the war, standing in the front hall and being smiled down at by a lady with a vague, rather twittering voice and a cloud of pale hair. Was she my mother? I didn't think so, although she appeared to believe she was. After the comforts, the stoked coal fires, the scones and jam provided by Mrs Alves, the gamekeeper's wife at The Kennels, this vision was confusing, as was her claim to have taken over my mother's role.

'Did you hear?' my mother cries out. 'Christopher, did you hear? I knew it.'

My father is in his late seventies and gives the impression of having heard nothing at all. We're all three of us – my mother and father and myself – sitting on the terrace of the house that was – as I saw it – the Last Redoubt, the house on the coast of the Greek island of Corfu, where the sea stretches out to Italy and, the house being roadless, only the most intrepid visitors could come.

'At Glen,' my mother insists. 'Wanting to be called Mummy. In the war. Pamela – '

'Pamela?' says my father, and to avoid the lurch of terror I had experienced the summer before, when my parents came on a visit to our cottage in the country and in my mother's absence I brought up the troublesome subject of my other half-brother James, I walked a few steps down the terrace and pretended to pick a bunch of grapes from the vine there. For I had understood then that my father remembered nothing of the woman he had married and stayed married to for ten years, before divorce and marriage to my mother; he had kept his first family at Admiral's House in Hampstead, and Glen came to mean nothing more to her boys than truncated school holidays. Until the war came, of course. Then, so it seemed, I had been claimed by my father's first wife: after all, what better preventative to rescuing me could there be than all of Europe closed to my real mother's return?

My father begins to look uncomfortable, as he had at the time of the country visit, when family matters were brought up and my mother wasn't there to change the subject for him. This time, for which I felt pathetically grateful, my mother has only gone indoors to fill a jug with water and place some agapanthus blossoms in it before coming out again and holding it near my father, so the reflections of the blue flowers shine for a moment on his white shirt and he smiles contentedly.

'Lovely, darling,' my father says, twisting his head to take in another glimpse of the sea he has painted ceaselessly, a landscape in his new – and last – home, which is radically different from that surrounding Glen. I wonder if I can ask him what he thinks – or whether he thinks at all – about the fights and feuds over Glen, or whether he misses the beauty of the place he was never tempted to paint. But I know I can't – and that I don't need to anyway. I know somehow that my father may have forgotten Pamela, but however deeply buried Glen may have become for him, it is still as present as the dinosaurs and distant planets he tried to tell us about in those long, freezing hours in the war.

CHAPTER SIX

Glen: Childhood

The hat is on the long table in the Hall – the big, pillared room my mother denuded of its baronial past, panelling, antlers and all. Nanny and old Mrs McKay are standing in front of the table and laughing and saying, 'Lieutenant Tennant' – or so I realise today, when thinking of the peaked, khaki piece of headgear that sat on a table usually reserved for mail or, on occasion, a trout on a plate still only half an hour from death and wearing an agonised expression. 'Lieutenant Tennant', as I soon came to understand when I followed Nanny up to the nursery, was my half-brother Colin. He was in the army now.

The trouble with his visits, so I also came to understand, was a lack of punctuality. He couldn't get up for the dried egg that constituted breakfast in the pantry, by the warming cupboard. He was still asleep when, in a brave recreation of the old, pre-war days before the servants left, Tibbie made a muffled summons to lunch on the gong at the far end of the Hall. He would play the piano at any time, or the ancient gramophone would wail 'Creole Love Song' or Maxine Sullivan singing 'Loch Lomond'. These were selections which belonged to him alone; the records were my mother's, a late-thirties medley I never tired of. But my – or I should say 'our' – father, waiting in the arctic dining-room, standing by a tepid hotplate bearing rabbit in a bright-orange paprika sauce (Agnes the cook had come over just before the war from Czechoslovakia), accompanied by sullen-looking boiled potatoes, was only too ready to lose his temper. Where was Colin? (James, not to my mother's delight, was first into the dining-room every time: without any sense of sharing, he would take all the peas.) Aunt Anne and her husband Philip (he was Philip Toynbee, her first husband, drunk, as I learned when I was older, whether it was lunchtime or breakfast-time or teatime) were already at table and eating when Colin came in. The famous temper, the temper which only its owner could lose as Head of the House, would explode in the dining-room that looked down the valley through a curtain of horizontal rain on most days of the year.

My mother liked Colin. I don't know whether she was aware of the lateness of his rising or if long waits for lunch got on her nerves. She left all the temper scenes he wanted to my father, and gave only a vague impression of alarm or sadness when his fist went down with a shout or a thump on the polished mahogany table. Anne, as I recall, looked very anxious, and the next most worried was probably me, for I'd made my father angry a few times and been terrified at the thought of retribution, although I was never punished or even reprimanded when the squall had passed.

Neither of my parents, or even Nanny, knew of my own attempts to rouse this appearing-and-disappearing brother in time for porridge and dried egg (both undesirable and thus perhaps responsible for my lack of success). A confirmed Freudian would have had no trouble in detecting incestuous desires in the child who crept along the corridor each morning past the room that belonged to James. The boys had two adjacent cells, identical and like their rooms at school, which possibly, again in Freudian terms, showed a basic desire on the part of our father to settle down happily with his second family and forget, as he later came to do, the existence of his first wife, with little thought given to his sons. But I would put a high bet on this suddenly-arrived brother simply enjoying the game.

I can't have been more than seven years old, my age when the war finished and before we all went south to London, to school and a flat in Bryanston Square. My father had returned to the family business in 1942, after a disagreement with the Special Operations Executive, of which he had been head in Cairo. My mother was often in London ambulance-driving with literary friends. But I remember, on an occasion when she must have been at Glen, the delivery of a slim package, taken up to her room by Tibbie. I was in there at the time, perched on the bed next to the remains of a frugal breakfast tray, and I watched my mother tear at the hard cardboard before extracting a new novel, *The Sheltering Sky* by Paul Bowles. More than that – other than my efforts to dislodge the somnolent figure in the cell down the passage – is lost to me. The tugging at the eiderdown and thick brown blanket, I do know, never had any success. A thin slice of the sleeper's back, one ear and tousled hair half pulled under a sheet, were immovable – thanks, no doubt, to an iron grip under the bedclothes. Like the novel just received by my mother, the cover seemed to personify the object within: hard to open, and as mysterious when it did finally emerge as it had been when still encased in wrapping.

CHAPTER SEVEN

Glen: Alone

'So what did your friends think of the man you chose to marry?'

We're in a village house, my mother and I, in Corfu – the big white house on the sea has been sold, but because my mother has Greek domicile she's decided to keep a presence here, in a house I share with her. We're in a 'good village', as places are labelled round here ('bad' usually means there have been, or still are, Communists in charge of the municipality; 'good' signals a conservative regime). Glen and the early years seem a million miles away – and only his paintings, reminders of my father's happiness in Greece, make it credible to bring up a subject as impossibly remote as my parents' engagement and their marriage at Caxton Hall in 1935.

'I suppose they thought he was – well, old,' my mother says after a minute of thought. 'And he was – '

'He was thirty-five,' I say – but then, thinking of her fellow students at the Slade, I go on: 'Did he seem . . . old-fashioned? I mean, there seems to be a big jump between 1925, when he married Pamela, and ten years later. Was he considered a fuddy-duddy? And most of your friends must have found you marrying a peer quite ridiculous.'

'Oh, not at all,' my mother rushes to defend my handsome father. 'It was all right.'

45

I've learned to steer away when a past situation is said to be 'all right': it usually signals something complicated, if not actually forbidden. 'Gilbert and Maud Russell took Stanway, in Gloucestershire,' my mother explains when I persist further, asking how she and my father met. 'In November for the pheasant shooting.'

'Oh,' I say. I can't imagine that left-wing literary people in the mid-thirties would have enjoyed the idea of spending time with a pheasant-shooting lord. And I remember, when I was ten or eleven years old and living in London with my parents, how a visit to them in our home in Chester Terrace from my mother's sister's husband Philip Toynbee would end with him dashing to the nearest pub. I had twice bumped into him at the corner – but he invariably put on speed and only a wolfish laugh stood for a greeting as he ran.

So I'm left with my father's Edwardian-ness, if such a word can be coined. The man my very modern mother had chosen to marry had first been met in a stately home. Stanway, with its famous oriel window, stood right at the top of the list; worse, it actually was the house of the well-known beauty Mary Elcho, one of the three Wyndham sisters painted by Sargent at the beginning of the century. Mary Elcho was my father's aunt. His mother takes centre stage in the portrait, the first Pamela, the woman of whom, my mother confirmed, my father never spoke, stating that he 'didn't like talking about the past'. Yet here, in this nest of Edwardians, she had fallen in love with him, and it was clearly a whirlwind romance – they met in November 1934 and married in March the following year when my father's divorce came through.

46

I'm trying to imagine how all this came about when my mother describes the wedding day: lunch with her parents, the train journey up to Scotland, old Mary McKay as she came forward to welcome my mother on the first day of her marriage. 'I wore a tailleur,' my mother says, when I press her for details of her appearance. And I see now that the short dark hair, the well-cut suit and her air of maintaining an impression of casualness combined with a refusal to look 'radiant' as brides were – and still are – expected to be, does indeed place her a great distance away from my father's first wife. Pamela – the second Pamela in my father's life, and the god-daughter of his mother, the first Pamela – comes from another world from my mother. Her wedding photograph is posed outside Wells Cathedral in Somerset ten years before my parents, oblivious of the cameras, walked through the crowd at the register office to start their married life. The other Pamela stands marooned against the biscuit-coloured stone of the cathedral: her head-dress and bridal gown proclaim the 1920s and contain no hint of the coming of a new age – and it is almost a relief to examine the shot of Margot Asquith as she jumps out of a taxi and runs to greet her nephew Christopher, my father. Something about Pamela's garb demonstrates a need to be 'lovely': no one would imagine this bride, a contemporary of my father's, to be a Cambridge graduate and a member of a distinguished, clever family. Trapped in lace and satin, she looks ready to Charleston her way through life. My mother, in her understated dark blue, seems to make no concessions to what may be expected of a newly-married young woman: she will please herself and will make no effort to please others.

'Of course,' my mother says, as the pile of photographs reveals a study of her looking straight at the camera: here there is more than a suggestion of Louise Brooks. She is answering my question as to whether divorced people's weddings were quieter in those days than church ceremonies with all the trappings, and as she replies I realise it's only recently that huge, lavish weddings for those who have been married before or have children already (an unthinkable state of affairs at the time) have become the norm. Civil weddings were kept quiet: the word divorce was, like the ludicrous brown and white 'co-respondent' shoes which formed the core of so many jokes, as unacceptable as (another chestnut) the night in Brighton with a sham prostitute, the divorcing husband and his improbable adultery exposed by the arrival of early-morning tea.

So I move away from my father's determined stride at Caxton Hall and – because I wonder how he avoided marrying one of the young women only too anxious to ensnare this obviously good catch once it was known that his marriage was falling apart – I ask my mother who the other contenders were. I knew they were Society women. Ava Waverley. Lady Pamela Berry. Paula Jellibrand. There were doubtless scores of others. And I begin to see that my parents isolated themselves from Society life and liked it that way. There were few invitations to grand neighbours to come to stay or dine at Glen. The Wolfe-Murrays over the hills near Peebles were true friends – but, looking back, there really was, save a wartime visit from Cyril Connolly from the south, or a protracted stay by the much-adored Micky Burns, a dearth of entertainment. (Family, of course, was something else, but such juxtapositions as that of the snobbish Clare, my father's sister, to my mother's father George Powell were hardly conducive to wanting to push the boat out.)

'Once you were married and had come back from Turkey – '

'And Toby was born,' my mother says. 'In June 1941 after the round-the-world trip we had to make to get back – '

'Didn't you invite people to Glen? You must have been lonely when dad was in London. You once said you were frightened, going up to bed . . . '

'Especially going up the big staircase,' my mother says. 'Not that I ever saw anything. It's true, only Tibbie was there, miles away down a corridor, but – no, it was nothing really.' And for a minute she does look haunted. I know she's thinking of my father's mother, Pamela, with her séances and her obsessive love for her son Bim, who was killed at the Somme. Little wonder my father didn't like talking about the past.

'But then it all changed,' I say, and as I speak I feel my past loneliness lift like mist, blown away, transforming the long, solitary walks I would take as soon as I was old enough (and often even if I wasn't), up through the black pines and larch trees of the Larknow wood, on to the heather and the ravine above the loch, with its rattle of falling stones as I slithered across.

In my mind I've gone along the side of the Berks, the range of hills that hold Glen. When I walk up higher I'll be able to look down at the house, my favourite view, with Glen and the old kitchen garden laid out behind it, where I go hunting for dog violets in spring.

'Did it change?' my mother asks, looking taken aback at the certainty in my voice. 'You mean the Buccleuch wedding, when people came to stay.'

'No, before that,' I say.

'Do you mean – ?'

'Yes. When he invited those girls to Glen,' I say. 'I must have been about twelve years old.'

'Oh, Colin,' my mother says.

But I am already up on the turreted roof and watching for the car that will bring these glamorous guests up the drive. I see myself as I run down to catch them on the front doorstep. I see that in turn they hardly see me at all.

And then I'm indoors and it's night. My mother and father have gone up to bed. I follow the girls up and up, to the tall spiral staircase on the first-floor landing and then beyond, to the Clematis Room, where one of them will sleep tonight. We all fall into the four-poster: the three girls and Colin – and me, pulled in by the strongest and plainest of the girls, Kate. We are going to play charades.

'Venetia, Kate,' my mother remembers, 'Pandora. She was awfully pretty. What happened to her, I wonder.'

For once, I'm not interested in what my mother knows, or wants to know. I want to get away from there, but I can't: imprisoned in the four-poster in the Clematis Room, I feel my life unwind and then change its course.

CHAPTER EIGHT

Glen: The Engagement

1955

I'm walking along the side of the Berks, looking down at the small stretch of water they call the Henwives Pond, and I stop for a moment, listening to the sounds from the farm, wondering if my father is going round with the factor. When I was young I was allowed to come too, to stare at the pigs and the cows as if something might suddenly happen to them, they might metamorphose, like the animals in the fairy tales by James Hogg in the library at Glen, into three-legged stools or the like. But there is no sound of voices. It's a quiet day altogether, very white and calm, a 'pearly Peeblesshire morning', as my father's Aunt Margot wrote in her journal of the place she loved when it was like this. It's the kind of day that looks full of itself – even the clouds are plump, floating in the mother-of-pearl sky as if it makes no difference which direction they finally decide to take. There's a sense of infinite patience – or usually there is – on this bare hillside with its irregular stretches of heather and short, greying grass. Nothing will ever happen here, these are the oldest hills in the south of the country – so my father says, warming to the subject as we go further back in time. Immeasurable centuries ago, these hills were like this. Nothing

51

happened then, and nothing ever will. Except today – when my elder half-brother brings his fiancée to meet us for the first time.

'Don't stay out for too long, darling.' Now I do hear a voice, it's the voice of guilt, calling me back to the house, to the soft shuffling sound of Tibbie as she brings in a tray with coffee and biscuits. The very fact of its arrival alienates my mother, who never has coffee and biscuits. But isn't that what she will want, this stranger who will one day lay new carpets and walk through our house with a gliding step? Even imagining what is expected of us makes us both exhausted: we feel the boredom and tiredness of people who are doomed to live in a hotel.

Of course, I've been selfish, stayed out too long on my beloved mountain. The car – a black Bentley which takes my father and a chauffeur to the City every day when we're in London (a recent driver, saying, 'Do you like snow, my lord?' was surprised by the answer he received when he tried to push cocaine: 'Oh yes, I like snow,' my father amiably replied) – is by the front door and it is empty. She – 'she' is all I can call this unknown addition to the family – must have met my mother and father by now. By the time I've run down the Hall – what did 'she' make of my mother's green-grass flooring, I wonder – the coffee might have been poured and my father would have refused a biscuit – again I knew that it was my mother who would feel a stranger, offering biscuits to a husband who had never been tempted to eat one. Who were we – what play was being acted out at Glen that day?

'She' is not only beautiful, but as pale and immoveable

as the marble pillars which famously adorn her ancestral home. A snob's delight, an entry in the register of nobles and courtiers that far outshines any Balfoor or Harcoor that my brother could dream up, 'she' is the first incomer to the family of the present generation who will improve the standing of the family as he sees it. Marriage to my mother had, in Colin's eyes, lowered the importance of the Tennants even further – his mother Pamela had at least been the god-daughter of the sole claim to nobility in the family, Pamela Wyndham, our father's mother – and he had a restless Lady Muriel on his mother's side to boast about. But things had slipped badly since the old days, when the thirteen offspring of the Bart had jumped into the aristocracy without a moment's hesitation. It never occurred to me, I may add, that I would be expected next to come up with a suitable viscount to take to the altar.

CHAPTER NINE

London, 2008

I'm trying to gauge my mother's reaction – in the flesh this time – to Henry's claim that our distant cousin Bella is due to inherit Glen. 'Very dynastic,' a friend older than I am remarks when I ask him whether he thinks it is true, or not. 'But a lot of people at the time thought Bella was down to be the one who'd get it in the end. But who knows – and who cares, really?'

I don't know if I care, but being told you are about to have an unexpected stranger in your family home gives you a funny feeling – as did the assurance that loads of people had heard about it. It's thinking back to that day at Glen when I came in late from the hills to meet my future sister-in-law – and wanting to know, finally, what my mother thought of it all – that has led me to ask if she believes Henry's story on the day I was wrapping presents in my flat nearly twenty years ago.

'No, I liked her very much. She was terribly nice.' My mother has changed the subject, concentrating on her feelings for Colin's wife, and has swerved away from the unpleasant subject, which, like so many 'family secrets', can be believed and disbelieved at the same time.

'But when "she" first came to Glen – his fiancée I mean – did you think she was the right person for Colin? You always said how much you liked Pandora – do you remember her?'

'Yes, Pandora was – well, I did like her, why they didn't marry I don't know,' was all that came next – and I, now visited by the memory of the Clematis Room at the top of the spiral stairs, Colin lunging under bedclothes as he went at the three girls and the recognition of the strange emotion I suffered then, both excited and excluded, at twelve years old, withdrew from the subject much as my mother had done.

'I wonder what "she" thought of Colin's first day in the office,' I say – for both my mother and I are fond of him, and like at the same time to laugh at his inventions and excesses.

'What was that, darling?' A day at C. Tennant Sons was hardly likely to be memorable after all these years; besides, although she is very sharp and can understand anything that comes up in conversation, my mother now seems to veer away from direct questions. The very mention of the family business, sold in the early 1960s, must belong in the Jurassic age as far as she is concerned.

'You know,' I can't resist urging her on, 'when Colin got engaged he decided he was going to be a reformed character . . . he'd never been to Tennants and he was nearly thirty – he lived in that flat off Lowndes Square and Lucian Freud painted him . . . '

'Didn't he collect all those Victorian pictures?'

'Yes, Atkinson Grimshaw.' I start laughing, because a vision of a mews house, the cramped ground-floor flat full of paintings either just bought or sold, comes to mind. 'The first day at the office, everyone noticed that Colin still had his pyjamas on, under his suit . . . '

'Honestly!' my mother says, laughing.

'And that was the time,' I say, 'that he told me his new resolution. It was just after the announcement of his engagement. He said, "I'll never make another joke." '

Now we both laugh, as if Colin were in the room making us listen to the jokes he has given up. But, I think later, nothing is clearer as a result of our talk. I don't know what my mother thinks of any of the stories she has heard over the years. I don't even know what she thought on that day at Glen, when the beautiful marble fiancée came for the first time. One comment my mother made stays in my mind. 'She' was offered a drink before lunch by my father (we all drank powerful dry Martinis, a sign of the new American invasion, along with fridges and sports cars). 'That's what I don't understand,' my mother remarked afterwards. 'She said, "I'll just have a gin and tonic." Why is a gin and tonic somehow purer – did you notice that?'

CHAPTER TEN

Glen, Summer 1954

The summer holidays are here, and are greeted with dread by my mother. As in a recurring nightmare, my father's sister Clare and my mother's father George will somehow be unable to avoid coinciding dates. On this occasion, Clare has embarrassingly suffered a jilt, the elderly general to whom she had considered herself engaged having sacked her with the deathless words, 'Let's face it, we've had it,' a statement my brother Colin loves to repeat when the aunt, known as Purplemouth (greasy, fuchsia lipstick and white-face-cream-smothered cheeks), is just within earshot. But Colin can do no wrong by now, as far as I am concerned. The dull, quiet days at Glen with only my unenterprising parents are galvanised by his jokes and laughter – and even when he is away, letters come displaying an army of fascinating Swiss or Italian stamps and containing pages of 'advice'; this, Colin assures me, is essential for a girl my age. He has modelled the letters on Lord Chesterfield's famous correspondence.

Before his arrival, there isn't much to do except wander about the valley, ending up from time to time at the loch, which has bright black water and is freezing cold. I used to swim there when I was a child, but I'm fifteen now, and hardly have the energy to lower myself into a rowing boat, so great is my impatience to see the one visitor who will change the summer holidays beyond imagining. I shall be witty and appreciated, like my Aunt Clare (whom Colin sometimes resembles, as I conclude when my admiration turns to doubt in the coming days). But for now, Glen itself mirrors my mood: swathes of lurid purple heather lie on the flanks of the hills; the trees that are the remains of the Ettrick Forest show silver trunks and dancing green leaves, as if autumn and winter were, like the awaited brother, threatening never to come. And as I wait and fidget on the wooden seat that abuts the loch, I wonder why Colin seems only a visitor, when surely he can stay as long as he wants to at Glen? Why does he seem so foreign, in the house he will inherit, a house which has been lived in for four generations by his – our – forebears? Are 'broken' families always like this, the elder siblings strangers to the new regime? It didn't occur to me, on that day when I longed for him to come north – to tease us all, including my good-natured mother who simply laughs when 'Colonel Powell' (her father's name, but why can't he be addressed in more familiar terms by Colin?) makes one ridiculous remark after another – that his teasing was my elder half-brother's way of distancing us. I, as a girl, could be influenced and shaped, away from the new family that had excluded him. Girls were expected to change their names anyway, though heaven forbid the union that fails to supply a good substitution: an Honourable as husband, at least, or, if not English, a Principe or a Marques was the type of name-change applauded by Colin. Now, as I walk down to the house from the loch, I'm smiling as I try to guess whether the car has come yet, and if so, will 'Colonel

Powell' push out on to the front step and wobble there, self-importantly, to greet his daughter's stepson? 'Colonel Powell' will surely by now have wobbled over to the drawing-room drinks tray a few times – it's already past one. Anticipating Colin's arrival and the laughter we'll go in for as soon as he jumps out of the car, I put on speed and half-run to the last, steep brae and the outer stretches of the garden. 'Colonel Powell' is the son of Prince Louis of 'Battenberg', Colin says as my memory replays last summer's excruciating family holiday. And I see my mother shoot her eyes skyward, half amused by the parentage given to her father. It's true, the Colonel can't pronounce his 'r's', but only Colin could have given him royal ancestry as a result of this minor problem.

I'm drawing nearer. Here is the grown-over bomb shelter by the wicket gate. Once, cans of food were stored here – but the war was a long time ago and no one except myself can remember that only one bomb ever fell, over the hills beyond Black House in a place called Mutton Hall. The German plane came down after it. But only Nanny and I and the wireless were at Glen at the time – and I don't know why I wasn't sent to The Kennels or whether Colin and James were staying up at the Robsons' in the head (then, as a result of the war, the sole) gardener's house to get away from the London bombs.

*   *   *

The circular drive is empty when I finally arrive, breathless with anticipation, by the stone archway in front of the house. No car is here – looking through into the stable block converted to garages, there is no car there, either. A dreadful sense that something more 'amusing' has happened. (One of Colin's Italian friends has a habit of calling from Rome and asking if it's amusing in London; Colin's stock response is: 'I'll go and look out of the window.') But how could he allow this to happen? He is going to a series of grand balls in Venice in September and has hinted he'll take me along.

My mother's face went very still as he spoke of the Volpis and the Robillants, but whether she was totting up the expense of dresses if this went ahead, I don't know. My father had money worries – the tax he paid on his income made it, he said, more economical for him to do the laundry himself than continue at C. Tennant Sons in the City – and a general financial anxiety, instilled in me for as long as I could remember, was topped up by Colin's confidences, delivered like rifle shots when our father was safely out of the room: 'He lost everything in the 1929 Crash, you know – he had a stockbroker in New York who kept saying, "Double up!" and he did and was wiped out. It's his fault there's no money here – all his fault.'

If I'd been more grown up when these judgements were passed, I might have questioned Colin more closely. But a man of twenty-five attired in costly suits (Roberts in Savile Row) was too formidable an adversary to take on and I tucked this information away with Colin's other disobliging accounts of my father's conduct where money was concerned. (My mother, for some reason, escaped censure, although she was, along with my father, always good for a laugh.)

When I try to think of that August day at Glen – the loneliness of waiting, the run for two and a half miles from the end of the valley to the house – all for nothing, or

worse, for a sense of emptiness and disappointment, I
conclude that this day marked the very slight and uncertain
beginning of a new appraisal of Colin, whom I had known
only from the time I left real childhood behind, at about
twelve years old. The flicker was so slight that it vanished
almost as soon as it came: it had come only to refute the
sense of unquestioning adoration I knew I had for this
strange, entertaining half-brother; and it was not lacking
in judgement, or even, for the shadow of a second, fear.
What frightened me was the sense of being shaped: I had
no alternative, now I was caught in the web, to the quick
response I was expected to give on every occasion, whether
sad or glad; like him, I was a master of repartee and found
myself applauded for my attempts at wit. I had persuaded
my reluctant mother to permit me to leave school at the
end of the summer term – that is, in the summer of 1954;
the law prevented me from leaving earlier by insisting that
all sixteen-year-olds take School Cert, an exam I passed
with a distinct lack of flying colours. I wasn't even sixteen –
how was I to live on my amusing sallies; how could my
mother ensure I continued my education? Of course, the
ignorant and lazy daughters of the privileged classes went
to Paris for a term or two, grew into débutantes in white net
dresses and prayed they would marry as soon as possible.
But somehow I was already too old for this; I was worldly
beyond my years; and it was the recognition that if I
continued as I was going along now I would give up everything of value – like friends of my own age, or a real desire
to learn something more lasting than the *riposte*, or the
ricanement (why are the words describing ridicule all

French?) – and would then be lost, never to find my way out. I would giggle all the way to the void I had learned to dread.

This moment, however, passed quickly, and by the time I had climbed the front steps and made my way into the grass-green Hall, my need to be praised for a joke and appreciated for my general appearance had overcome my slight apprehensions of a brief time before. Colin must be here, by now; my mother would look worriedly at me as I dashed in, going straight for the pile of gramophone records, determined to find Maxine Sullivan's 'Loch Lomond' as if to underline the bogus Scottishness of Glen at this time of year. With Hollywood-purple heather rampant on hills that came down as far as the terraced garden and Aunt Clare got up like the heroine of a romantic novel in a Tennant tartan kilt (the tartan invented in 1908 in the northern town of Elgin and providing rugs, kilts and other Scotiana apparently indefinitely, for all the efforts made to hide them away in shame), there was plenty for us to laugh about.

And so we did, as Maxine's liquid tones filled the drawing-room and caused my father, who had just given up smoking and was prone to fits of temper, to rise from his armchair and walk firmly out of the room. Neither my newly-arrived brother nor I paid the slightest attention to this. My mother's father, after extracting an old-fashioned-looking sweet (he called it a 'bonbon') from a small silver box kept in his pocket, pulled himself to his feet and lumbered across to offer me – the only child in the room, as he saw it – one of these undesirable sweets. And it is here – as I look back on the sense of unease that had come to me on the way down from the loch – that my impudence went too far. 'No thank

you, Colonel Powell,' I said, already shaking with the laughter
I knew would be shared from the fireplace, where Colin stood,
bright eyes gazing, waiting for the bait.

'Colin, can you find me the sheet music for some of the old
songs – it used to be on the piano,' came at this point from
Aunt Clare, who had clearly not understood the rudeness of
my cheeky reply to my mother's father. Clare goes on: 'We
could have a singsong tomorrow night, perhaps – when she
is here. "I *Do* Love To Be Beside The Seaside" – I can play
that, you know.'

This was beyond laughter – but I can no longer catch
my brother's eye. The guilt that follows imagined mis-
behaviour – or half-imagined, half-real is nearer the mark,
perhaps – takes hold of me as I return to the scene, for
'Colonel Powell', suddenly red-faced in indignation, is pulling
me to the door as if to evict me, return me to the nursery
where I must learn manners – and he pushes me with
unexpected strength out into the Hall and the door closes
fast in my face. 'I'm your *grandfather*,' are the only words he
will say. And I have to wait, in the shadows of the Old
Drawing-Room across the Hall, where family portraits stare
down at me and the cold of the August evening makes me
shiver, along with a sense that something is happening here
at Glen tonight and I am the last to know.

After an age of waiting, my mother comes out of the
drawing-room but, as if I have become suddenly someone
else, she appears to fail to recognise me. What is she doing
out here?

'I'm going up to bed,' my mother says, but without looking
at me directly.

'So early?' I ask, knowing there must be another reason than simple tiredness. She usually enjoys the times when Colin comes, there are games to be played, and jokes. Has 'Colonel Powell' complained to her about the impertinence of her daughter?

'I must go and talk to Tibbie. I just don't know where we're going to put her – she won't like the back stairs, Colin says she's terribly grand,' my mother goes bafflingly on.

'Who, who?'

'Ruby,' my mother snaps.

'Ruby who?'

But my mother is going with a grim determination to the door that leads to the back stairs – the area which may prove unpopular with this new visitor, whoever she may be.

It's only later when I dare to slink back into the drawing-room that I begin to understand what has taken place here tonight. My father has disappeared; only Colin and Aunt Clare remain at a card table where he is playing patience and she sits commenting on the sheet music that must have been found somewhere in the pile of Scottish ballads and Chopin nocturnes my father so hopes not to have to hear.

There has been bad news, that's easy to see. But it takes several minutes to take in Colin's decision of where his guest will sleep. 'The Princess in the Valley Room,' he says, 'and Ruby – that's her maid – in the dressing-room is the best. There's plenty of time, she won't come until teatime, we can arrange it all in the morning.'

Neither of my parents had ever expressed any interest in – or potential affection for – any member of the Royal Family. Even I, at my particularly disagreeable stage of life in those days, can see that springing the news of this unexpected visitor is, to say the least, upsetting for my mother.

'I'm sure Christopher won't mind giving up his dressing-room,' my aunt says – although she cannot have any idea whether my father would go along with this or not. 'Now, what song shall we choose?'

CHAPTER ELEVEN

The Preparations

It doesn't happen to many fifteen-year-old girls to find themselves appointed hostess to a famously demanding and bad-tempered member of the Royal Family, yet as far as I remember, I felt nothing other than delight in imagining myself chosen as my elder half-brother's partner for the weekend. Waiting for the arrival of the Princess was another matter: I hung around in my bedroom, driven there by Aunt Clare's attempts to regain her piano-playing gifts in the drawing-room; I went often to the bedroom on the first floor which looked out on the stone arch at the head of the drive, where Salve and Vale were inscribed in 'ancient' lettering (as if guests needed to be told whether they had just arrived or were leaving: 'Arriver c'est partir un peu,' as my mother's friend Cyril Connolly had proclaimed on a rare visit to Glen).

Time had never moved so slowly. Colin, fussing in pantry and dining-room over placement, candelabra and the like, made it clear that a matter of such great importance as the first dinner of the royal visit could not be left to my mother. My father, obviously, would have had no idea how to arrange a table or where to place the fish knives – known to be common since Nancy Mitford's embarrassing U and non-U piece in *Encounter*, but we were having fish for the first

66

course. 'The Guards eat fish with two forks,' said Colin in a low hiss of anxiety, but this was of no help to anyone. My mother was subjected to her stepson's clenched announcements; 'No butler! No butler!' was one of these, but short of dressing the gamekeeper in some kind of indoor servant's outfit, she could only point out that there was clearly no solution to this problem. Tibbie and a girl from the village would hand round the salmon mousse, followed by the grouse. My father, who had paid a brief visit to the cellar, also vetoed champagne. After all, as we knew he was thinking, the coming meal was not the celebration of an engagement. Red and white wine would do.

Or would it? As the royal limo still made no sign of turning up and disgorging its long-awaited passenger, there was plenty of time to turn over this possibility. It would be hard to say which of my parents prayed more earnestly that my father's eldest son had no intention of proposing to the Princess once the gentlemen had rejoined the ladies after port and my Dansette gramophone had been switched on in the Old Drawing-Room. My mother, shy by nature, must have dreaded the rush of publicity that forging this new relationship would bring. It was almost a political decision on her part not to make speeches – or, worse still, to appear to see herself as a superior person in public. My father, who once confided his preference, when it came to talking to God, to 'go up on the hill and speak to Him privately', would loathe the rituals and ceremonies associated with being part of the Royal Family. Only Colin – and myself, I have to say: I shared my brother's genes after all – clearly felt that a welcome excitement had entered our family at last. People would confirm our specialness; no one would be dismissive or rude.

By seven in the evening, panic had begun to set in. Did Colin get the date wrong? (Highly unlikely: this was the day on which he had concentrated all his energies since coming north for the summer holidays.) Had there been an accident? My mother was so nervous of tumbles and crashes that visitors' small children were pulled off the steps in the garden, even if several yards from the plunge to disaster, and held firmly as they wriggled to get free. Most imponderable: had there been a row? But with only one telephone in the house (in the basement next to the locked wine cellar), we would all have heard if the romance had entered a stormy phase. Besides, my brother had clearly appointed himself as chief courtier to this 'daughter of an Emperor', as he had proclaimed his awaited guest to be. He revered her – there could never be misunderstandings or difficulties with a person so much higher in the hierarchy than any of us assembled at Glen on that August evening could possibly be.

CHAPTER TWELVE

The Narrow Escape

SUMMER 2009

'So did dad really take Colin aside and tell him it was never too late to back out?' I'm repeating what a family friend, her name Paula Jellibrand, told me on a walk at Glen in the winter of that disconcerting year. (Paula had been the only one to treat me as a grown-up and a confidante when I was eleven or twelve: yet, however sophisticated I might have appeared to be, it never occurred to me that this ex-beauty, early wearer of trousers, who exuded an air of a kind of triumphant singleness, had in those days monitored my elder half-brother's every move because she, like so many others, was in love with him.) 'I can't see how there could have been time,' I go pedantically on, as my mother pretends to look out of the window at the London pedestrians, some clutching green bags for their shopping, others weighed down by plastic. 'I mean, James never left them alone, for one thing. Colin kept kicking him as he stamped after the couple – '

'No one wanted to have Princess Margaret to stay,' my mother says in an absent-minded tone. 'She expected so much – but I suppose' – referring to the ease with which Colin had persuaded her (and my reluctant father) to invite

Princess Margaret to Glen in the summer of '54 – 'she was much younger then.'

There was no doubt about my mother's determination not to reveal secrets of my father's sudden bursts of temper – for surely, he must have terrified his eldest son into reneging on the marriage proposal the national press as well, it seemed, as the entire population of the British Isles were eagerly expecting on the occasion of the royal visit.

'So James saved us from a dreadful fate,' I say half-jokingly.

'James,' says my mother in the same dreamy tone. But I know, as I look back, that I have forgotten, or half-forgotten him too. It's too painful now, to refer to this younger brother of the wizard Colin, the one who so obviously showed his jealousy and sense of unfairness, whose tales were all of loss. 'My sovereign was lost in the kitchen garden; Colin lost it . . . I caught fish in the burn, someone took them, they're gone now.' These woes come plaintively back to me as I look with some irritation at my mother gazing at the grey West London day, seemingly unable to remember the time royalty came and nearly wrecked her quiet life. Surely she, too, must have felt a vast sense of relief when no proposal came, the kind of feeling you don't often forget. She had been spared a total change in her way of living; she would have expected to present herself to the world. If my father had shown his anger and apprehension at the prospect of his own marriage at risk if an engagement went ahead, then the observation that it's never too late to back out achieved its desired effect. How frightened of his father Colin evidently was at that time only came to me much later.

So James has been batted away again. Both my mother and I sit in silence while the truly terrifying episodes to do with James unfurl before our eyes. The time, on a visit to Glen, when he went to the pantry just before breakfast and, seeing two trays with toast and tea, announced that I had poisoned my mother's tea as a revenge for her affair with my 'lover', a (homosexual) friend who was staying in the house. The accusatory letters, carried around in a briefcase by my ageing and forgetful father; letters which complained about a lack of money but actually showed a terrible lack of love. How could we have got on to James?

CHAPTER THIRTEEN

The Arrival

I'm in the Hall at Glen, down at the far end where bookcases
with the tall books are kept: Audubon's flowers and birds,
all valuable in the extreme, as I later discovered when my
father was no longer there and the pictures and library,
disposed of like the cows driven away from the farm on the
estate, were bundled up and placed in a van to go to
Sotheby's or Christie's. The preponderance of books here,
though, are the Game Books, bound in vellum, which
recorded my grandfather Eddy's successes and disasters on
the moor or on the River Tweed, which provided salmon
fishing about two miles away, by the haunted house of
Traquair. (That Eddy, husband of the formidable Pamela,
had a long-term mistress there was of course never
mentioned – although my mother, in a rare spurt of con-
fidentiality, told me she had been a 'nice woman' and, as far
as I can remember, my mother also said in those days that
she was still alive and I had seen her on the infrequent
occasions when she came to tea.)

For all the possibility of excitement and intrigue, however,
my grandfather's Game Books were deeply distressing.
Expensively presented and handwritten by the Laird himself
(Eddy was ennobled by his brother-in-law H. H. Asquith in
1914), their records of animal and bird deaths always filled

me with gloom and apprehension. How could anyone indulge themselves in this frivolous saga of slaughter? Why was it that most of the men named in these vellum memorials met solely when they could go out to kill? Eddy died in 1921 so I never knew him, but I couldn't help wondering if 'Colonel Powell', certainly not a landowner, wasn't the preferable grandfather after all? Eddy's regular good looks and fair, curly hair caused me to hope, nevertheless, that I would find him interesting one day.

Colin, obviously, could only laugh at my mother's father, who was ignored except for the times his invented origins as a Battenberg had another airing. Who was he and where did he come from? This question was implicit in every remark directed at my poor grandfather. And in London, in the mews house already visited by foreign royalty before the longed-for contact with Princess Margaret was achieved, I saw on one of the visits there – visits that I longed for with the same intensity – that a new joke of 'Colonel Powell' had been brought down to London.

'Colonel Powell on his honeymoon,' my elder half-brother announced as we stood gazing at the most recent picture taken from an attic at Glen and destined for the saleroom, a painting by G. F. Watts entitled *The Moon and Endymion*. And we all laughed. My grandmother, wife of the Colonel, my mother's mother, had died less than two years earlier, and this luscious portrayal of what resembled a blend of the Kama Sutra and a Pre-Raphaelite portrait of a mythical scene, showed – so Colin proclaimed – my maternal grand-father's new wife, Ena. But for all my brother's desire to find a new joke ten times a day, the baiting of the Colonel had to end with the introduction of the second Mrs Powell. Without hearing Aunt Clare's muttered comment, on the newly-wed couple's first and only visit to Glen – 'impossibly common' were her half-whispered, half-whistled words – I recognised that this wobbling, puce-faced old man, my grandfather, whether I denied him or not, would no longer be seen even as a Battenberg.

* * *

The car is here; it doesn't scrunch on the gravel of the circular drive in front of the house but comes quietly, as if the men who have been polishing and sweeping, some of them police and others mysteriously sourced labourers from the village or the farm, have succeeded in making the arrival of the daughter of an Emperor a silent, almost magical event. There is no clock in the Hall, perhaps reflecting my mother's dislike of being told the time: she has never worn a watch; the household settles into her own rhythms; and on the rare occasions when the front doorbell is pushed and a peal of sound comes into the downstairs rooms, people look first at their wrist-watches, as if any unexpected sound must be a summons from Time.

I don't know where I was supposed to be at the moment of the Princess's arrival – and it's too late now to flee or to stand in readiness for the curtsey I have been taught by my brother to make. I'm aware, in a way that is rare at home, of the absence of other people, for being at home on an ordinary day doesn't involve wondering where others may be. I rehearse in my mind the introductions Colin will make once his important visitor has mounted the steps and entered the small hall hung with pictures of dead and bleeding animals, surely familiar (if not welcome) to the Princess. But where is everyone? I stand petrified: is my father even now on the front doorstep, what is left of his prematurely white hair stirring in the cool wind that runs through the place all summer, rustling the leaves on the birch trees, turning Tibbie's hands blue when she comes down from the kitchen garden with radishes and spinach in a wooden basket? Has everyone suffered an attack of shyness and gone to their rooms? In the case of Aunt Clare, this would hardly be probable. It is late, though, she may have decided to change into evening dress; the question won't have occurred to my mother, and now it is too late to change, she should be greeting the visitor on the front step, surely, along with my father? And where is Colin?

Standing frozen by the table at the far end of the Hall, I realise I hadn't noticed the huge, leather-bound Visitors' Book, set out by Colin surely, the book where the voices of the past lie trapped, their owners coming out to walk or glide on the carpet that is worn thin here by the shuffling, racing feet of players at a neighbouring ping-pong table. Of course – he must want to draw attention to the signature of Oscar Wilde and other famous people, of Gladstone and Asquith and the rest . . . He must hope that his guest will be impressed, as he is every time he brings the great marbled volume into the open and the ghosts of those who have loved Glen throng the long Hall.

This is the hour the dead walk with the living, in this pocket of suspended and cancelled time. All the coming scenes are here, waiting to be projected on the white walls and long windows; all the past events and feelings and vanished vows are here to bring together the dead and weave them into the fading picture. I hear the whisper of skirts, the stamp of a thin cane as I bend down over the mausoleum of names that is my brother's greatest treasure.

*   *   *

The door of the inner hall, a long way behind me at the front of the house, opens and closes. I can feel the draught of air, and I can hear a voice – my father's, I think, but sounding jolly, almost boisterous, in a way that isn't recognisable: is everyone affected by the presence of royalty, not just my elder half-brother but my father as well? (It would take years for me to accept that telling your son there's always time to back out of a possible engagement doesn't clash with showing delight at the arrival of the putative daughter-in-law.) My father, for all his dislike of the idea of living in a monarchy, became changed, his voice forced and his laughter hearty: only my mother, wishing no doubt that her sister Anne was there to bring in reminders of the lives people actually did live in post-war Glen – knitting interminably; shivering by a sparse log fire; counting coupons; praying for blue skies and the long poplar-lined avenues of Europe, too expensive to visit and currency restrictions daunting – only my mother, inaudible and too quiet-voiced to be heard from this distance, would have remained herself on such an occasion.

I will be 'found' standing over the Visitors' Book, I realise; and in turn I feel myself become another person – the younger sister this member of the Royal Family will perhaps have been told briefly about, the fifteen-year-old girl who must be even as undesirable to meet or talk to as the Colonel will prove to be. After all, we have nothing in common except Colin, and I have no conceivable 'news' that either part of this romancing couple could find even remotely worth hearing. I bend lower, the pages of stiff cream paper go back . . . and I find the one signature I need, the mystery signature which appears to indicate providence at work, a proof of the power of coincidence and prophecy. This can be my 'story'; I can become interesting; I can show the Princess that I am part of an interesting past.

Lily Walsh was her name – later I discovered she was known as 'Widow Powell' – and here it is, as the door of the inner hall stretches open as far as it will go and people begin to walk through. Here is the name, 1902 the date, written in a faded blue from the pen of a half-century ago. Lily Walsh, who came to stay at Glen (although no one knows how or why or whose friend she was). All I have been told by my mother is – to Colin's immense delight – that Lily Walsh was none other than my mother's grandmother; she was the mother of the Colonel, and no one knew anything about her apart from the fact that she had been invited to Glen in 1902. Her signature sits next to that of Violet Bonham-Carter, but there is no evidence that they were friends or even knew each other. Who was Lily Walsh?

The bunch of people who were in the inner hall has now made its way along the Hall and pauses somewhere between the cold, dark room known as The Old Drawing-Room, this filled with blue-and-white Chinese vases and still painted in the dreary beige mustardy colours of the 1920s, and the main staircase leading to the bedrooms and the spiral staircase with its little rubber bricks to prevent slipping on the way down.

They will go up – they have gone up – the main staircase. A cross-looking woman rises on the stairs behind the royal party, and I see the anguished expression on my mother's face. (Why hadn't it occurred to me that they would take this path to the first floor? How could I have imagined that no effort would have been made to include me in the introductions, either by my parents or my brother? How I had shrunk, in my own estimation.) And to make it worse, I guess that the cross woman is Princess Margaret's maid, Ruby: filled with the sickening bile of jealousy, I tell myself that there would always be more attention paid in this house to a previously unknown guest (if Ruby could be so described) than to my parents' own daughter. Anything or anyone who might prove disruptive at Glen provoked anxiety – suppose Tibbie was in some way put out by Ruby and so on. For the first time, I pray that the anticipated engagement will take place – I'd had sympathy for my mother's dread, but now I wish a thousand summer house parties on her, with all the impossible menus and the sheer horror of after-dinner games, and the embarrassing relations – while I promise myself that I will be a very long way away.

*   *   *

The Hall was long and dim and dreary, as I stood in the aftermath of my pique, brooded over by an alabaster bust of my great-grandmother Emma. Looking down from her blue pedestal, she was a reminder of my past expectation that Colin would linger on my 'wickedness': 'My sister – next year she's being taken on a trip to Australia and round the world, but she wrote "Damn the World" on the wall, in London.' Then the pretence of shocked laughter and, as I had pre-played the scene, a look of secret admiration from the royal guest. It was true that my father, as chairman of the Northern Assurance Company, was due to visit Australia the following year, and that – having complained after an earlier trip that the games of after-dinner postman's knock insisted on by his hosts had been something to avoid at all costs – he might take my mother and myself along with him, but I had shown little interest in the idea. The attack on the globe, so rudely worded by Colin's younger sister, may or may not have been pencilled on the cold blue-painted wall that I remember in the little room by the kitchen in the London house, which had been allotted to me and my school friends. It seems unlikely, now – at any rate it's the kind of 'outrageous' detail my brother loved to make up.

CHAPTER FOURTEEN

Summer 2002, Fulham

I'm with my mother and my aunt in the small house bought
by my aunt about a decade ago, when her way of life and
her natural modesty led her to sell the tall stucco building
in South Kensington that had been her home with her
husband Richard Wollheim. Naturally, I liked the grand,
tall house in Pelham Crescent, with the smell of dusty
books and the portraits by the Italian Communist artist,
Guttuso; I liked the way people sat at the trestle table in
the kitchen for literally hours after the meal had been
eaten (all cooked by the pink-faced Anne, her fair hair
falling over her eyes and continually pushed back as the
joint came out of the oven); and I liked not knowing what
any of the subjects discussed, whether literature or philo-
sophy, could actually mean to anybody. So when some time
after Anne and Richard parted she bought the narrow
little house in Fulham, I was disappointed: in order to find
excitement and glamour in North End Road, I started
looking for the origins of the woman my mother knew
nothing about and my aunt claimed to have no interest in
whatsoever, Lily Walsh.

'Oh I don't know,' my aunt says.

'But she was your grandmother,' I point out, silently
wondering if my mother and Anne are the most secretive

women on earth: I mean, what's wrong with trying to find out about your own grandmother?

'In the tin box,' Polly, Anne's daughter, volunteers; 'in the attic,' goes on the successful *Guardian* columnist, whose relationship with her mother is certainly more frank and free than my own with Elizabeth Powell, who married my father in 1935 and never permitted the display of a photograph of the happy pair on their wedding day as they left Caxton Hall, heads down, as if just sentenced to life imprisonment by the registrar.

'Not this attic,' Anne says in a crisp, final tone. It is possible to imagine that the whole move, from Pelham Crescent to the far reaches of Fulham, was accomplished in order to leave the 'tin box' behind at the previous address. 'But what was in it?' I asks, noting that both my mother and my aunt have made identical efforts to avoid eye contact, resulting in them staring at each other like strangers on the Tube.

My mother, unusually, is the first to break the silence. 'Mrs Keppel used to come and see my father,' she says. 'His mother died young – '

Mrs Keppel? I suffer the familiar dread, instilled by Colin years before, of any mention of the Royal Family. Surely, Alice Keppel had been King Edward VII's *maitresse en titre*? As the term comes dancing horribly back to me I can hear my brother's meticulous voice as he read aloud from the *Almanac de Gotha*. ' "Un marriage que ne conforme pas aux lois de la famille," ' was one of his favourites, when forgetting what I was supposed to have learnt on the subject of morganatic marriage, he told me its meaning again.

'Mrs Keppel was a friend of – ' my mother begins, the coolness in her voice indicating that she knew these people's names entirely by accident.

'Lily Walsh,' Polly contributes. But it's clear the political journalist has no interest in an Edwardian past for our family.

'Was she a – ' I find myself beginning. I feel I'm now seen as a romancer, a bodice-ripping detective who wishes to sell an ancient kiss-and-tell to the *Daily Mail*. Why, I ask myself bitterly, did I bother to try to find out in the first place? But then the great slab of the Visitors' Book swims up before me. What was Lily Walsh doing there, and why are her granddaughters so reluctant to allow her an existence then or now?

'Mrs Keppel took George [the Colonel's first name] under her wing when . . . when Lily died.' It's my mother speaking but I'm visited by a dreadful possibility: not only are my mother and aunt possessors of knowledge denied to me, but that knowledge might indicate the true ancestry of the Colonel. I see him wobble along the Hall at Glen, a half-consumed third martini in his hand, and I hear Colin's mocking voice as he teases my mother. So was the Colonel a 'Battenberg' after all? Would I never escape the smear of royal snobbery?

'I think the tin box is here,' Polly says earnestly to my aunt. To her, I realise, it's a matter to be investigated then disposed of. 'I'm pretty certain we left nothing behind at Pelham Crescent,' she goes on. 'I could go up to the loft, mum . . . '

'Lunch is ready,' my aunt replies.

*   *   *

But as I had imagined, it was never the right time for Lily Walsh. My mother informed me, at least, that Lily was 'the daughter of an Irish clergyman'; that she had come to London, where she was known as a 'pretty woman'; that her friend Alice Keppel kept an eye on George, as he and his brother were still young at the time of Lily's death.

The conversation was changed, after that, my aunt looking as bored by the subject of the 'pretty woman' (did this mean, in those days, a courtesan, even a tart?) as she had on previous occasions when the name of Lily Walsh had come up.

But there was more to it than Anne's determination to stop me from delving too deep into family secrets. My mother, polite and uninterested in such a colourful grandmother, had let out on our way to my aunt's house (I had gone in the hope of finding Lily, as often before) that George (as she called her father) had found difficulty in joining a regiment at the outbreak of the First World War. 'He didn't know his father's first name.'

'But he was called Powell?'

'Yes. And someone paid for him and his brother to go to Eton.'

'Someone without a first name?'

'Well, yes, I suppose so . . . '

Lunch passed pleasantly, as it always did when my aunt was in charge: there was talk of friends we had in common, and who loved her, and there was a quiche which my aunt admitted after much teasing that she had made herself, despite its professional, shop-bought appearance. As we sat and chatted and sipped the very black coffee – which reminded me of those after-dinner sittings at the table in Pelham Crescent, when the philosophers and the painters and potters sat until long after midnight at the scrubbed pine table – I knew that it would be a simple case of bad manners to bring up the whereabouts of the tin box. Short of burgling my aunt's house, my hands were tied; I knew it was up in the attic, however much she denied it, and I began to suspect that the box's contents were something of which she was deeply ashamed.

CHAPTER FIFTEEN

Mooning

SUMMER 1954

I had changed into a white, green-spotted muslin dress (Horrocks, possibly; at any rate nothing too expensive or showy, and chosen by my mother in Oxford Street as suitable wear for a daughter of fifteen) and had gone down the small staircase into the Hall, when I realised I had no idea of how I should enter the drawing-room, whether I should curtsey straight after going in, or make my way (I saw myself stumbling and falling in an attack of shyness) to the sofa where Princess Margaret must by now be ensconced. How I could now be late when I had waited, fruitlessly as it turned out, for so long, I had no idea. 'Mooning,' my mother would say, but more often to herself if time passed and she found she had come down just before Tibbie sounded the gong for lunch. In response to an imagined interrogation on the subject of her lateness, she gave 'mooning' as the reason. (That the word now means something else entirely has not been accepted by my mother.)

I had not been 'mooning', I had been smarting at the absence of the jokes and the admiration – of the companion-ship on which I counted – of my brother. I could never be outrageous again, or surprising, or witty: I was a husk of

85

the self he had created and nurtured over the years. I could no longer see myself in any role on this occasion when I most needed to exhibit an interesting, sophisticated personality: who I was and who I could possibly become were entwined in an empty pool of shadow, of nothingness. As I could no longer be picked out – or even seen – I had stayed in the icy bedroom allotted to the elder daughter of the house, known as the Doocot; I stood frozen by the miniature four-poster I had outgrown years before. I possessed a little clutch bag and in it I found the black eyeliner pencil I used to circle my eyes and make butterfly wings at the side. Protected by my eye shadow (blue, bought in the local Boots), and hedged in by a prickly mascara, I had spent so long on my new armour that distant voices in the main Hall below me seemed to belong to a mythical time – teatime, even – and I was left stranded; I had hidden myself so successfully that my eventual descent seemed a matter of indifference, a roll of the dice. Now, if I couldn't recognise myself, no one would know who this stranger could possibly be. But I was, unavoidably as I saw it, late.

CHAPTER SIXTEEN

The Clootie Horn

When I was about seven years old I could see the devil, much as the woman could who walked into the kirk at Alloway to pray and found herself in full view of a maddened bullock, its horns trapped in the pew above. I'd heard the story of the young son of 'Auld Glen', friend and neighbour of Robert Burns and his father William, and his eventual freeing of 'Old Nick' as the terrified woman looked on. He'd known it was his father John Tennant's bull, which must have rambled away from the borders of his land and been cornered in the kirk: it made a funny story which reached the ears of the poet at Alloway and inspired the masterpiece that was the poem *Tam O'Shanter*. It took hours to get back to sleep, once May had finished reading or telling the ballad of demonic possession where a beast 'black, grim and large' plays wild music on the pipes and makes the dancers 'skirl'.

When I was still very young I was proud to show visitors the horn said to have come from that beast in its stampede to get out of the kirk. For years, the horn was in use as a bolting tube on Auld Glen's farm in Ayrshire, for the administration of medicine to the cattle. Then, as seemed to happen to almost anything in the family, it attained value (a silver mouthpiece was fitted and it was placed on a marble mount in the Old Drawing-Room) and was said to have been used as a kind of early Tannoy system, the town crier in Ochiltree announcing on blowing into the 'Clootie Horn' that it was time to go to work. That this imperative was delivered by an appurtenance of the devil himself must have got people going. In my own case, when I lifted it from its aristocratic resting-place at Glen, it seemed evil, almost alive: to hold a devil's horn was an experience not granted to seven-year-olds at the Glen village school, and I think some of the children there saw me as a descendant of 'Old Nick'.

'It's no yours, it's God's,' a boy told me as I ran, bossy from the start, to claim my place on the playground seesaw. For all my protestations, he was certain, two hundred years since the incident in the kirk at Alloway, of God's dominion and the devil's – and I definitely belonged to the devil's patch, in his eyes.

*   *   *

Humble beginnings had little chance of real interest or respect, in most of the family's opinion; the one-roomed buildings, the huge families, the smoke escaping from the classic hole in roof: all these needed the glamour of Robert Burns in order to make them mentionable, and apart from the Clootie Horn and a first edition of Burns poems, there wasn't anything much from that era to show off about. Talking in a weird 'Scottish' accent was felt by some to be amusing but certainly not by my father's mother, Pamela Wyndham, who famously turned her eyes away if having to pay a rare visit by train to Glasgow, where billboards lining sooty walls on the approach to the city where the family fortune had been made proclaimed C. TENNANT SONS & CO. LTD, all reminders of the first Tennant chemist and his huge St Rollox chemicals factory. The fact of an ancestor's resilience – Auld Glen was one of them – in the face of the difficulties of farming, the early deaths of children and the struggle to provide an education went unmarked by descendants of those who had walked ten miles to a funeral and had shared a box bed with many others.

John Tennant, further down the line in the second half of the nineteenth century, was accepted, if grudgingly: he was the true capitalist, the founder of countless companies – but apart from the fact that his gloomy portrait closely resembled Colin's younger brother James, there was little to say about this self-made millionaire, other than that his 'partner' or 'companion' Robina Arrol had not married John Tennant except in the Scottish way, which involved posting a notice on the front door announcing the pair to be joined 'by habit or repute'. 'Perhaps she had been married before,' said one of my great-aunts primly (no less than three of the aunts toiled on a family history, and all three were festooned with medals and peerages before they died) – but no one wanted to go further and discover the true life and origins of the red-haired Robina. She had been an employee at the factory, after all, and only a generation and a half away from the man my father's mother had married, Sir Edward Tennant. The two large portraits of John and Robina hang half-hidden at the top of the main staircase. They would have been visible to Princess Margaret on her way up – but by virtue of the great height of the part of the Hall where they'd been placed, obviously of no great importance to anyone.

CHAPTER SEVENTEEN

Great Aunts

How could Peggy, Nancy and Kay, the three daughters of Sir Charles's second marriage and born in his late seventies, have begun to understand the lives of their many bulbous-nosed, canny and (compared to the well-to-do or aristocratic in their part of Ayrshire, the Earls of Glencairn and their families) stunted forebears? All three sisters went on to do good works, it was true: they mixed with all kinds, but in a photograph taken in the early years of the twentieth century, where the youngest sister is shown in the arms of her nanny, by the front steps of Glen – the nanny had been with the family for sixty years, longer than the house – the sheer volume of ribboned organdie and sleek baby carriages demonstrates that there was little lacking in the way of comfort in Sir Charles's establishment. There were other homes, too, for the children, both grown-up and infant: a house in London in Grosvenor Square and another in North Berwick, built especially for the new wife Marguerite and her children.

Surely the family could hardly be blamed for their obsession with Sir Charles. His portrait showed him with a nose that, quite unlike those of his ancestors, was needle-sharp: he was accustomed to picking out the lurking gold-mine in India, or overseeing the stitching together of companies in mergers or new collaborations. When guests came, my elder half-brother would pause in the Old Drawing-Room facing my favourite picture – a girl on a hill, *Collina* by Sir Joshua Reynolds – while Sir Charles was quite over-looked and forgotten. 'Lady Gertrude Fitzpatrick, daughter of the eighth Earl of Gospatrick – ' my brother's voice selected words with care. When it enunciated the noble titles, it seemed to reprimand Sir Charles, hung opposite the earl's daughter, for his astonishing business acumen. Colin, perhaps, wanted a fortune that was freshly minted, but desired an old title as well as a dash of third-generation decadence.

*   *   *

I mixed together the superstitions and fairy tales, the magic foxes and the tales of transmogrification provided by the shepherd James Hogg, some of these stories set in a wood of ancient silver birches that was a part of the Ettrick Forest and was directly opposite the room next to mine, the Valley Room.

CHAPTER EIGHTEEN

'Wabster Charlie'

By the time the great-aunts' book came out, my father had been living for ten years in Greece, and it seemed unlikely, when the package was fetched from the taverna in the village at the top of the hill where mail was collected, that he would have much desire to read about the forebears who had made his emigration and last years by a blue sea possible. Did he need to be reminded of the struggles of all the Johns and Davids and Williams (there were no women in the great-aunts' tales of Scottish enterprise)? Did he – who, I had once heard him confide to my younger brother, was surprised Italy was 'allowed to have a Communist Party' – have any wish to be told of one Charles Tennant of the late eighteenth century? ('Wabster Charlie' in Burns's poem–letter to the family, a man who was on the side of Napoleon, who stood up for Queen Caroline and who led his eight-year-old son – the Sir Charles whose portrait faced Collina's at Glen – to march with the Chartists in 1832.) My father had inherited the tendency to vote Liberal from his Aunt Margot and her husband Prime Minister Asquith, and in London the *News Chronicle* was delivered daily to our house – but were the beliefs of 'Wabster Charlie' of any interest to him now?

It was true, he liked the story of the fearless 'Wabster', whose efforts were always to defend and protect the other weavers thrown out of work by the introduction of new machinery – and, as it was repeated often, it grew the incantatory powers of the stories I liked to tell myself. The legend was that Charles, searching for the solution to the conundrum of how linen and cotton could be bleached without the wasting of so much time (sheets were left in bleaching fields to dry in the infrequent sun; trains carried the material at speed to the north and the machines were ready to deliver the orders long before a few feeble rays had succeeded in bleaching the stuff), had been spotted by a wealthy neighbour and praised for pacing his bleach field each day at an early hour. The marriage of the neighbour's daughter to 'Wabster Charlie' duly took place – and the young weaver-scientist was able to forge ahead with his inventions, chlorine liquor contributing to the solution of the bleaching problem.

CHAPTER NINETEEN

Cigarette Smoke

SUMMER 1954

You could tell, at Glen, whether the drawing-room had emptied of its guests and the second – and most dreary – part of the evening had got under way across the Hall in the dining-room, or whether some guests lingered by the drinks tray (last chance of a shot of neat spirits until late), by the smell the room gave off, almost palpable and caused partly by the scented stocks and lilies my mother had placed in tall cones of glass or alabaster and partly by the alcohol itself. An invasive stink of gin signified the devotion paid by the Colonel to the dry martini or a strong whiff of bourbon that my father had mixed an old-fashioned – maybe several – for a new guest who would enjoy the glacé cherry and the lump of sugar soaked in Angostura bitters (both of these newly available at Ray Martin's grocery in Innerleithen, and a clear signal of the nascent boom).

The smell, strong, sweet and herbal – from the ingredients proffered in the making of a Manhattan or a whisky sour or in the voguish preparation of a lemony vodkatini – instilled a longing for this hour to last for ever. The ghosts I knew so well had retired to their funless quarters, for no lady would drink before dinner until well after the First World War, and

94

even the Doocot, frequently so noisy with chat from Margot and Laura, fell silent and grey, the dull blue walls supporting the one picture over the fireplace – a train crossing a marsh or prairie, its lonesome whistle only too imaginable in the room where, as on other nights, I would clamber into the doll-sized four-poster and try to sleep. The difference between this and previous periods of darkness when they came creeping towards the house was of course that later – tonight when it finally came – there would be someone next to – very near to – my own room. It was a strange layout, for the Doocot, fairly spacious as it was, appeared cramped once one had come in and looked to the left, to a small area with a wash basin and a mirror above which reflected a long tapestry curtain just a few feet opposite. The room began to seem even more constrained if one went to the curtain and pulled it back an inch or two, perhaps to confirm that a hanging cupboard for clothes had been fashioned in the alcove there. Unexpectedly, behind this arras of green and red thread, thick as the Morris hangings of which my father's mother Pamela had been so proud in her day, was nothing less than a flight of three steps, these thickly carpeted, as if to ward off any noise or interference from the Valley Room next door. (And the other possibility would also present itself: that both curtain and carpet were there to stop intrusive sounds from the Doocot penetrating the largest and most esteemed bedroom at Glen.)

Here – within earshot either way of a stifled giggle or the run of a zip in an expensive dress – up a flight of steps and through a sturdy-looking door painted white as any other bedroom door, Princess Margaret would lay her head on a pillow, when the evening was finished with and all that could come was sleep. A strong smell of cigarette smoke seeped down as I pulled the curtain back and forth; and it was this that I followed down into the Hall, there pausing and wondering whether to turn right into the drawing-room, with its cocktail aroma, or left to the dining-room, a room that was cold even at this time of year and looked out on horizontal rain – or on pines in a smudge of dark green and brown that stood in the valley and would provide Princess Margaret with her view.

CHAPTER TWENTY

The Pownie Goes to Edinburgh

I found a woman I could think about in the family – and I
see her, sometimes, in a thick grey-blue skirt bundled up to
the knees as she scrubs and dusts at Glenconner, the farm
at Ochiltree in Ayrshire where Auld Glen brought up two
families of children. Agnes, who married George Reid of a
neighbouring farm, Barquharrie, was John Tennant's eldest
daughter (she had seven sisters and as many brothers) and
she died aged twenty-three, leaving two daughters. When
Burns the bard found himself famous he asked to borrow
the Reids' 'pownie'; and on 27 November 1786, the poet set
off for his triumphal visit to Edinburgh, promising to send
the animal back the next day, by carrier. Did Agnes complain
when instead of the pony Burns sent a note from the capital:
'I hope you will forgive my not returning him by carrier. I
left Mr Prentice's on Monday night. There was a most
agreeable little party in the evening . . . .'

The great-aunts tended to look on the bright side – the
Tennant and Burns family members are exhaustingly described in their book as contented, vivacious, satisfied with
their restricted diet and eager only to improve their minds
(how the daughters of a Victorian millionaire pioneer of the
Industrial Revolution could feel assured of their forebears'
delight – especially at going to a funeral – it is hard to

97

say) – and left me at liberty to sympathise with poor Agnes Reid. In my thoughts she is always waiting for the return of the 'pownie', perhaps in love with Burns herself, as so many women were, and dreading the breaking of the news to George Reid, her husband, that the beast is clearly not going to be returned. Agnes mirrored my own uncertainty and discontent with my life – for just as I waited for the transforming agent our royal guest would surely prove to be, making us all famous (though not through our poetic talents, it must be said), so Agnes became, as she waited, perhaps unable to believe in the evident carelessness of a childhood friend, a member of the upright Burnes family (as they then spelt the name). No worker on the land was free of the fear of poverty, then: for all the great-aunts' assurances of the happiness of devout ploughmen and floor-scrubbing lasses, I knew, somehow, that Agnes and George had struggled to stay alive – and I knew for a fact that Agnes would die at twenty-three years old.

CHAPTER TWENTY-ONE

Down and Out

SUMMER 1954

The drawing-room is being tidied, in preparation for the re-entry of the guests when dinner is over: the Princess will fling herself down (or so I imagine) on a newly refreshed sofa – the sofa my father usually sits on, but he won't complain; even the most ardent republican is unlikely to tell a royal guest to shove along, or get up altogether if the exalted personage is ensconced when they arrive. And surely they will arrive; after forty-five minutes or an hour, the gentlemen will come in from sitting over their port, to be greeted by the ladies, who will have had to find a subject to talk about, a topic more exalted than shopping (and who would care to discuss the dowdy stores in Edinburgh at that time?) and if possible 'amusing', which I know will be taken care of by Aunt Clare in her light, clipped tones. Colin is needed at this time, when dinner finishes (have I really missed the whole thing?) and an evening stretches ahead, an evening turning to night: the hours are not circumscribed, but it must on no account be boring. Will I be expected to play charades, or the paper game 'definitions', where we have to guess a word when its bearer, a slip of the writing paper my mother keeps in the drawer of the writing desk, is passed from hand to hand?

Could there be a game of forfeits – an already practised way of banishing the Colonel from the room, as devised by my elder half-brother? Can the new guest find some way of scooping up her own little entourage and carrying them off to a room where they can enjoy each other's company and I – as I so desperately wish – will be counted among them, kohl-lined eyes, mascara and all?

No. I'm caught in the Hall, where I feel as if I've been trapped all day. Mrs Wilson empties ashtrays and walks past, drained martini glasses chiming on a tray; she is quite uninterested in the drama of lateness I'm acting out, by the chilly fireplace under the three-quarter-length portrait of a Scottish beauty by Raeburn. The cigarette-and-alcohol smell follows Mrs Wilson; now, holding a porcelain vase with drooping flowers in need of revival, Tibbie emerges from the drawing-room. But I might as well be a ghost: neither Mrs Wilson nor Tibbie can see me at all.

'Oh, here she is . . . Darling!' comes my father's voice: he must have seen me but is invisible behind the cedarwood panels of the dining-room door, which has closed again; Mrs Wilson has brushed past me and gone in to rescue the main course from the rattling lift in the pantry. Murmurs of appreciation rise as the door opens again and she begins a tour of the table, and as she goes I catch a glimpse of the feet of the birds, hanging over the side of the big silver serving dish. I feel sick at the sight and I transfer my gaze to my father as, very red in the face, he lifts a decanter of dark wine and turns to the guest of honour on his right. I know he is calling me, reassuring me that I've missed nothing, I can come in now.

The back of the eminent visitor is as plump and padded
with pale flesh as the game birds that are set down in front
of her. As she swivels round I see a bosom that plunges into
a low-cut black evening dress, and as she sees me standing
there in the doorway, I take in a dazzle of blue light from the
ear-rings and necklace and brooches she wears . . . and from
her royal blue eyes, wide open and startled when she sees me
there.

Then I'm rescued. I don't know if I curtsied or just stared
down at the floor (the whole business of obeisance and
royalty and the rest fills me, in this day of uncertainty and
change, with a new loathing and contempt), but I allow
myself to be taken firmly by the hand and led down the
length of the dining-table, to my seat between the two
middle-aged 'boys' who are the sons of Aunt Clare. They
were necessary, Colin said, to 'fill out the guests for later' –
although it was hard, seeing them in their Tennant tartan
kilts and little black velvet jackets, not to wonder what role
they could be expected to fill.

*   *   *

When Sir Charles sat at the head of the table at Glen, did he
envisage a royal romance for one of his great-grandsons,
was he as sure as my elder half-brother that a connection
with the British Royal Family was the most beneficial (and
useful) of all unions? Enough of 'Wabster Charlie', his own
father, lingered in him, I think, to make him wary of the
Establishment – until, at least, he found himself the father
of Margot, who married the Prime Minister H. H. Asquith
and ended her late nights in the Doocot, chatting to young

men impressed by her cleverness and rebellious attitudes to the too-easily accepted mores of the times. Would Sir Charles have been pleased to see the small, tight-waisted Princess at his table – or would he, perhaps, have taken the prospective bridegroom aside and told him it was never too late to back out – as Colin's father is supposed to have done? But he liked to allow his children to marry as they pleased – though what he made of his eldest son Eddy's wife Pamela it would be hard to say. He must have known of Pamela's sense of her superior origins, and her dislike of the industry on which the family fortune was based. It is even possible that he wondered why this beautiful and artistically gifted woman seemed to show so little appetite for the sports which engaged the interest – and gunfire – of the many sons among Sir Charles's thirteen children: would she never, like other wives and sisters, go out on the moor with the thick bread 'pieces' the kitchen made up, and stand in a shepherd's house while the dead birds were counted? Had Pamela been a problem to her father-in-law all along? Was she, as some with hindsight pointed out, a symbol of the coming degeneration of the family, this sad 'Mrs Edward' who spent more time with her ghosts than with real people and at the same time projected her image for the many male visitors, 'boyfriends' as a great-aunt pithily put it, when they came to Glen or to the house she loved best, Wilsford at the foot of the Downs that circle Stonehenge. 'Who are we preparating for today?' was famously asked by Pamela's children. No one could ever make out the blend of other-worldliness and ambition which made up Pamela.

*　　*　　*

At last it's time for the ladies to leave the table. I see that
as usual Aunt Clare is the one to give the signal: it would
be impossible for my mother to perform this antiquated
gesture – as it would have been for her sister Anne, who
brought her philosopher husband once or twice for Christmas
at Glen. (He made his feelings for the festive occasion
plain, referring to Christmas Day as 'Kippins' and intro-
ducing subjects deeply unpopular with his wife's brother-
in-law, my father: it was a relief all round when his visits
and his marriage to Anne ended and she came on her own
or with her children.) The men are standing, and for the
first time I dare to look round the table and not at the
reflection of my own face in the polished wood. I see the
two friends of the royal guest who have been invited to
keep her company – a small man, Johnny as I come to
know him, and a tall, vague-looking woman, Lady Elspeth,
who is, I think, the first chinless person I have seen. Then
there are Clare's 'boys', one ugly and the other handsome,
a prince and a frog standing together in their lace jabots
and invented tartan; and the Colonel, dangerously near the
daughter who most dislikes him, the pink-cheeked Anne;
and, between my mother and her sister, the much-excoriated
James, younger sibling of Colin and – as I remember from
a recent visit – victim of Colin's smashing of a gramophone
record over his head at the table when he had been 'boring'.

I shuffle out of the dining-room after the ladies, blushing
crimson as I trip on my long and now crumpled muslin
dress. The heat from the candles has caused my eye shadow
to run, and as I feel it creep down my face I reach for a
napkin lying twisted on the table and mop at the stream of

black mascara which now joins the blue, metallic shadow on its journey to my face's lower regions. I can no longer see clearly – and for this I am grateful, as my elder half-brother and my father are either side of Princess Margaret, and thus (presumably) doing all they can to distract her from the vision of a sister of a famously witty and handsome man ('a thing of beauty is a joy for ever' has been quoted by the *Daily Express* when referring to Colin) who has only to show off works of art or amusing sayings to inspire happiness. A wizard, a miracle joke-maker in whose company women blossom, heir – as the press likes to proclaim – to millions (the actual circumstances of my father are conveniently forgotten at a time like this), must on no account be embarrassed by a sister such as me.

'Not "out" yet,' I hear him hiss, as the royal gaze wanders over me. 'Not out' meaning I have not yet been presented at Court, so I couldn't know how to look or behave when in Society. 'My sister. Not yet out, ma'am . . . ' And he stands back so his eminent guest can lead the way into the frosty Hall.

'But then, why is she down?' I can see the royal blue eyes reflecting, as they sweep over me one last time. ('Down', as I know, means eating with the grown-ups in the dining-room. 'Is she down yet?' I have heard on the lips of my Edwardian Aunt Clare. But 'down for dinner' with the post-war Glen staff was inevitable. I was 'down' – and as I now saw, down and out as well.

CHAPTER TWENTY-TWO

The Ball

I am in the drawing-room; if you saw me from the back you'd think I was studying: my head is low and my jaw thrust out, as if the very thought of appearing attractive – or even grown-up – is of no concern to the serious person I am about to become. One of the reasons I appear like this, of course, is my awareness of my absolute loneliness in the midst of famous strangers (even Johnny has been interviewed about his long friendship with the Princess; another chinless person, a man this time known as Dommie, has driven across the Borders to join us and is vaguely recognisable from a group photo in last week's *Sunday Express*). And I'm just as abandoned when it comes to my own family: James, with his usual thoughtlessness, has sat down firmly next to my mother, who has assumed her where-was-I? expression, a mixture of vagueness and a sharp-eyed look, which goes with the forced proximity of the blundering, obsequious James. On his small velvet-upholstered chair sits the Colonel, who pulls the tarnished box of sweets from his pocket at two-minute intervals, snaps down the silver lid with a loud click, and then edges forward an inch or two, as if sitting on a toboggan that is coasting on a sea of *bon mots* to the acknowledgement of the splendid success of the evening. Then Clare, back very upright at the piano, voice high like the voice of an old child.

'I *do* like to be beside the seaside,' warbles the mother of the neglected boys, who devoutly turn the pages on the stand: abandoned in turn at the age of three and sent to a year-round boarding school, how could they risk losing one minute of her company on their brief holiday visit to Glen? Colin – he is behind me at the card table, sitting and chatting conspiratorially with his royal guest: no one can approach them for fear he is actually proposing marriage, even Mrs Wilson, who comes in with fresh ice for the after-dinner whiskies, walks on tiptoe as if interrupting an important rite. Dommie and Johnny are the only ones letting out laughs and loudly told anecdotes – perhaps they are in on the timing, and none of the rest of us are.

'Beside the seaside, beside the sea' – the last line of the charming old song – comes with greater strength than before, and my father, marooned on his usual sofa with Lady Elspeth, looks round irritably, as if wishing the instrument blown away, and this tiring and pointless evening with it. But then, although I am usually too preoccupied with myself to remember that my father has just given up smoking and Edwardian songs must act as triggers to his rage, I feel a wave of sympathy for him: how could my poor father have known, when he had found happiness at last with my mother (he once confided this to me, but our mutual embarrassment at this rare show of sentimentality meant it was never repeated), that this contentment might be summarily removed by a royal wedding and the succeeding duties expected of him as father-in-law of the bride? It is hardly surprising to find him morose and edgy on an occasion such as this. And Princess Margaret's cigarette, fitted neatly into an imposingly long holder, must be wafting its smoke down to him from the canasta table, where she sits with my elder half-brother: the brand is Du Maurier, which comes in a scarlet box reminiscent of the uniform worn by soldiers at the Changing of the Guard at Buckingham Palace. The entire experience must have brought my father to a rare state of depression.

The Princess gets up. She narrowly misses me as she picks her way to the sofa occupied by my father and Lady Elspeth. My father rises, and room is, naturally, made for her: bolsters and cushions part like the Red Sea to allow her in. She is handed a silver ashtray with a roofless tunnel on it – to hold the cigarette if its owner is talking or otherwise occupied – and as I push my straight-backed chair out of her way, I see that only a brown stub and a long column of ash are deposited in the place prepared for the slumbering cigarette, the uncovered silver tube. I see my father flinch and hear the metallic tones of the Princess's voice as she tries to engage him in conversation, and I see him shift from one foot to the other, as happens when he is being informed of something he doesn't want to know. A silence falls, the coming disaster flickers like lightning round the walls of the stricken room.

'Ma'am, shall we go to the ball?'

'Oh must I?' The understanding that she has been rescued from an unallowable period of silence comes through in the reply and those named as guests are rapidly marshalled to the drawing-room door and then out into the Hall. Johnny and Dommie, Lady Elspeth, Clare's two sons – all enacting the roles Colin has allotted them to fill out the party.

Everyone else, on their feet in accordance with royal protocol, has been left behind. I am the only one to stay sitting on my hard chair, until I decide to be near my father and walk over to him by the sofa. Now I am next to the Princess's cigarette – it has extinguished itself, only the column of white ash remains. And as I pick up the ashtray, deciding to move it as far away from my father as possible, I hear my name called out.

Colin invites me to come to the ball. 'In the Old Drawing-Room,' he shouts in his circus-ringmaster's voice. 'Ladeez and Gentlemen, the Ball!'

CHAPTER TWENTY-THREE

Dancing Partners

SUMMER 2007, LONDON

'So didn't you want to come and join us?' My mother has come over from Greece and I want to talk to her about my Aunt Anne who has recently died. Anne's daughter Polly has brought over the tin box from the attic in Fulham and surely my mother must be interested in looking at its contents – there are early photos of herself at the seaside, even the chauffeur they all hated, lurking in the background by the side of an old-fashioned-looking car. But we haven't got there, yet, and it's my fault: I'm trying to remember that summer of 1954, and the first evening of Princess Margaret's stay at Glen. All that happened is crystal clear except the ball, as my elder half-brother christened the small, ill-assorted collection of people dancing self-consciously to my little Dansette gramophone, dominated by the portrait of Sir Charles, the shadows in the room making his appearance even more wizard-like, pointed nose and all. Who was I dancing with? Johnny or Dommie? And whose voice is coming out from the grey box that is my small record player – is it Cliff Richard or even Frankie Lane, who Colin said made all the women swoon when he sang? Why is all that wiped out, as if the hidden meaning in the music of that time has been erased and the visit might never have happened? I can't say for sure, even, why I'm asking my mother this question – why didn't she and others come to Colin's improvised ball?

'Oh, we'd probably have been in the way,' my mother says. 'You know, all that fuss about Princess Margaret – Colin wouldn't have wanted us to crowd out the Old Drawing-room.'

'He wouldn't have wanted Colonel George,' I say, and I know as I speak that I've sounded cruel – 'brittle', a word often used to describe Aunt Clare, comes uncomfortably to mind. The thought of the Colonel stays with me, though, as my mother stares out into the cramped garden, still carpeted with the AstroTurf laid by the last owners and certain to invite disapproval from those in the family who live for elegance and chic.

'I feel guilty, thinking of him,' my mother says simply of her father. 'He suffered from shell-shock, you know.' (I didn't know and I feel a burning sense of guilt at the memory of the tricks and games that were played on the poor Colonel – like baiting a wounded and defenceless bull, I now realise.

'But did you think there was going to be an announcement of . . . of an engagement?' I press on.

And as my mother replies, 'Oh I don't think so,' I answer the question myself. Of course there was no engagement, there was a talk in the library between father and son – 'it's never too late to back out'. So in my memory we all danced on, and as my mother looks distractedly still into the narrow patch of the London garden I understand she has closed the subject for ever. 'What was brave of you,' she says finally, 'was that dinner party you were asked to give in London for Princess Margaret . . . in the autumn, soon after she came to stay. You weren't sixteen then – Dad and I were away . . . '

But I have no interest in that occasion. I think only of the end of the 'Ball' and I hear shoes shuffle over a parquet floor. The guests are leaving – Dommie will face his long drive into the Borders, Lady Elspeth goes with Johnny to a grand house near Walkerburn. I follow the remaining dancers out into the Hall to the small staircase, and, seeing the chief couples of the evening make their way up the main stairs – the stairs I had first seen them walk up, while I stood unseen below – I go fast down to the far end of the Hall, past the vellum notebooks filled with Pamela's ghostly proofs of a life beyond death, past my grandfather Eddy's rich, leather-bound tallies of sporting successes. I rise, leaping from one small stair to the next, and I emerge one storey higher, by the door to the Doocot. Here just beyond me, turning into the wide, dark bedroom passage, are my elder half-brother and Princess Margaret. They don't turn back or pay attention to me, and I hear a muttered good-night. I run into my room and close the door . . . my bright pink face, hastily mopped with cold water from the wash basin beneath the mirror, still bears smudges of black eye-liner. A faint breeze stirs the long tapestry curtain that conceals the three steps up to the Valley Room door. Did an opening and shutting door in the room above the three stairs cause this draught of air? As I stand in my oddly-shaped room, my gaze now fixed on the picture above the Victorian grate, of a train going across the dimly painted land, I see my grandmother Pamela, and I wonder, is everyone as lonely as I am in this family? Does a door open or close for anyone here?

But by the time I've thought this I am in bed and on the edge of sleep – and when I wake, as so often before, it is to a cold, blue room where the first thrust of light beyond the curtains shows the coming of another day.

CHAPTER TWENTY-FOUR

Glen: Disappearances

When Glen was made over to Colin in 1963, I was staying there, unaware of the change of ownership that had taken place, with my seven-year-old son, who was already as enthralled by the place as so many before him. 'Uncle Christopher,' a cousin wrote in a memoir, 'walks round the house with his hands in his coat pockets' – but by now this was no longer the case. My father was making plans to emigrate to Greece, where he settled in 1965. The summer guests no longer included the Colonel, although Aunt Clare still sat in August with her crossword puzzle and martini on the sofa in the (now carpeted in Tennant tartan) drawing-room. Books, treasures, paintings and other possessions collected by Sir Charles and by his son Eddy were destined for the saleroom – the principal victim of banishment being Constable's *Opening of Waterloo Bridge*, sold to kick-start its new owner's fortune. *Collina* was sold to the Columbus Gallery of Fine Arts, Ohio, and many other pictures were disposed of elsewhere, until an embarrassingly amateurish oil of Eddy in a boat was the sole work left to grace the Hall. The Marble Fiancée had married the new heir in 1956 and was subsequently appointed lady-in-waiting to Princess Margaret; Colin's wedding gift to the Princess had been ten acres of a small Caribbean island near St Vincent, Mustique.

CHAPTER TWENTY-fiVE

The Search for Oliver Hope

I was much older, by at least thirty or thirty-five years, when
I decided to look at the stories I had labelled 'Unexplained
Relations' – from the tall young man who had come to my
West London flat and excitedly informed me that Glen was
about to become the property of a mysterious cousin (I didn't
believe it then and I don't now: it was a fairy tale like those
in so many families, which come from a desire to leave a
mark, even if, as my old Nanny May used to say, 'you aren't
clever, funny or grand'), to the mysterious 'pretty woman'
who was my mother's grandmother, Lily Walsh. As well as
the unwelcome royal associations invented for the Colonel,
there seemed to be a whole host of lost family members
waiting to be revived and understood; and I came to realise
that while I stared in fascination at the likeness taken of
Lily in a photographer's studio in Montmartre in the 1870s
(the tin box had finally decided to yield its secrets, although
it was still impossible to discover who 'Widow Powell' actually
was), I was missing out on a story that belonged to my
paternal grandmother, Pamela.

It happened like this. In my parents' house in Greece –
in my father's study, where he sat puzzling over figures his
mind found it harder each day to cope with – a double
shelving of dusty files had accumulated. There was some-

thing 'forbidden' about opening them or looking at the settlements, the dowries, the specifications of land bought and sold to enrich one long-dead uncle or orders to be executed at the time of his death. There were details of beneficiaries – and of losers, the holders of preference shares in the now-defunct Tennants Estate Ltd, letters from lawyers and company directors and banks. It was obvious that no one had opened any of these for years, not since the time of my parents' emigration in the mid 1960s, and it was as if they were keeping a grumpy old man in a cupboard. The feeling began to grow in me that I needed to see these ancient documents. There might, after all, be some trace of my mother's wedding to my father. Pictures of my father at sixteen when he was sent off to Gallipoli had been discovered in a hatbox in the upstairs-landing cupboard: surely there must be something in the study to illuminate a family puzzle or two.

I found a deed relating to a bequest to a child adopted by my grandmother Pamela at the bottom of a disintegrating bamboo suitcase under the window ledge. Drawn up by Withers, the family solicitor, it announced the intention of Lord Glenconner to pay an annuity to one Oliver Hope, for the duration of his lifetime. The document was dated 1921, just after my grandfather Eddy died and my father took over the family interests. Bim, the oldest of Eddy and Pamela's sons, had been killed at the Somme; Pamela, after Eddy's death, married Sir Edward Grey in the church at Wilsford, with my father the only guest.

I decided to look for Oliver Hope. Who was he and why had he been left the annuity of fifty pounds a year?

Was he possibly Pamela's son with Edward Grey? Or was he descended from someone in the heart of the family – Pamela's eldest son perhaps, the handsome and captivating Bim?

*   *   *

I'd always known there had been another child in the family. His name was Oliver Hope and he belonged to the same generation as my father Christopher, his elder brother Bim and three other siblings (including Stephen Tennant).

But where he had come from, nobody knew.

The story was that Pamela, my grandmother, had walked into the infirmary in her nearest town, Salisbury, one day in 1916 and declared: 'I've lost my baby. Have you got one for me?'

Yet this story cannot be true. The enigma surrounding the 'lost brother' Oliver haunted me for many years; and I've yet to find him – he may well be dead.

The puzzle of who he really was, however, remains. This is the story of my search for Oliver.

My grandmother Pamela and her husband Eddy were Lord and Lady Glenconner at the time of this story.

They built Wilsford Manor in the early years of the century, and Pamela loved the place, positioned at the foot of Salisbury Plain with the River Avon flowing through the garden.

Her life should have been an entirely happy one. She and Eddy were rich (he had Glen, a turreted castle in the Borders of Scotland, and there was a town house in Queen Anne's Gate). Pamela was also a beauty, and, self-announced as 'unworldly' in an age of glitter and greed not so far removed from our own, she wrote books of poetry and stories for children. The Wilsford villagers liked the Lady of the Manor and in London Pamela was widely admired.

Yet there is evidence that my grandmother was far from happy in her life with my grandfather. Despite her great – and true – love for her children, whom she referred to as her 'jewels', Pamela was unfulfilled and turned to the world of spiritualism to find an answer to the pain she clearly suffered all her life.

Little did she know it at the time – but the 'psychical research' on which my grandmother embarked was to become the saviour of her life. Her son Bim – handsome and a gifted poet in his own right – was killed at the Somme. Pamela was to find his messages from the other world, with the help of the celebrated medium Gladys Leonard.

It would have made sense to discover that the child Oliver Hope had been adopted by my grandmother to compensate as far as possible for the terrible loss suffered at the death of Bim. 1916 – the year given in the legend of Pamela's visit to the infirmary in Salisbury and her peremptory demand for a baby – would have fitted perfectly. Bim was killed in September 1916.

I believed this to be the reason for Oliver coming into the family, for many years. 1916 had been a painful year for Pamela in other ways, too. She had given birth to a stillborn daughter, Hester, in March and had only six months to mourn before the favourite of the family, Edward Wyndham Tennant, was felled by a sniper in the First World War.

It all made sense. I would wonder about Oliver from time

to time – but I didn't feel I had to solve the mystery of his origins.

Not, that is, until out of the blue a fellow writer, Philip Hoare (biographer of Stephen Tennant, Pamela and Eddy's youngest son), sent me a copy of a weight chart made at Wilsford and dated July 1915.

Under the names of the other children – David (who went on to found London's notorious Gargoyle Club when he grew up) and Christopher (my father, who was sent off to the navy at Dartmouth at twelve years old) – was a list of scribbled names next to their weights. 'Roly' – this was the family dog. 'Gan-Gan', Pamela's mother Madeleine Wyndham. 'Edward', my grandfather, who at 9st 8lb was, surprisingly, the same weight as Gan-Gan.

I envisaged the scene. The lawn at Wilsford on a hot July afternoon, with yellow flag irises growing among the reeds bordering the Avon. The Manor, newly built but looking romantically old, with its ancient stone and a mass of pink roses climbing under mullioned windows. Pamela decides to while away this idyllic hour by recording the weights of her family. The big iron scales are brought out on to the lawn, along with a lined pad for her to write on. Nanny Trusler, the nurse whom, my father once told me, he had loved more than his mother, is there too. The children, Pamela's 'jewels', visited their parents after tea and had marginally more freedom than other children of the time – but Nanny Trusler was always on hand to whisk them off upstairs.

I saw the scene as I pored over the copy of the chart which Philip Hoare had sent me. Suddenly, near the foot of the list, a name in my grandmother's sloping handwriting stood out against the others.

Why hadn't I noticed it before? The hesitant writing gave an impression, even at a distance of nearly a century, of an uncertainty about its subject.

Oliver – 2st 4lb, it said.

It didn't take me long to work out that Pamela couldn't have adopted a newborn baby from Salisbury Infirmary in 1916 if the child already weighed over two stone in 1915.

Something odd was going on here. A secret had been buried and I wanted to know what it was.

Could it be that Oliver Hope – the name began to sound invented, the more I thought of it – had really been the brother of Bim and Christopher and David and Stephen and – the only girl – their sister Clare? Not just an adopted child of my grandmother's – but a biological one?

If this was the case, why had Oliver been left out of the family's bequests and inheritances? Or maybe he hadn't been forgotten entirely. I went to take out Philip Hoare's *Life of Stephen* and tried to discover what else the biographer had been told about Oliver – even though the information about Pamela's visit to Salisbury Infirmary had been patently untrue.

At the same time, I asked round all my friends for an estimate of an age to match the weight of 2st 4lb. I needed to imagine the scene on the lawn afresh.

'Two years old' . . . 'depends whether he was born large or small . . . ' I could have guessed that everyone would come up with a different idea of the age of the baby who once was Oliver.

But I was able to ascertain from a footnote in Philip's book that Oliver had been put in the Royal Navy (though it didn't say when),[1] and that my Uncle Stephen had sent him 'pipes and tobacco' to his ship stationed in Alexandria. These gifts continued to be sent right up to 1935.

Oliver suddenly leapt into adult life, from being a two-year-old on the lawn at Wilsford to a sailor on the far shores of a blue sea twenty years later.

His birth and the reasons for his coming into the family and then leaving it were as mysterious as ever. Had Oliver disappointed in some way? Had my grandmother tired of him? Or was there a scandal around the child, perhaps called after a famous orphan, Oliver Twist, with a quality of Hope attached for one who has to find his own way in the world?

I was determined to find out.

* * *

Phil Matthews was the first person I turned to in my search for Oliver. Phil lived near Wilsford in the days I used to borrow a cottage downriver from Uncle Stephen; and as a local historian who had renovated an old carriage in the stables at the Manor and seemed to know pretty well everything about my family and the area, he was just the right person to ask.

First, I was guided to Trowbridge Record Office. There, sure enough, was the register for Wilsford School, a red-

1 An advertisement was placed in *Navy News* for Oliver but there was no response.

brick building poised at the head of a steep bank overlooking the Avon. It was next to the cottage where I'd stayed, and I had memories of my son fishing on the slow-moving chalk stream all those years ago.

Again, I must have been daydreaming at the sight of the register, and it took me some time to realise that Oliver – or maybe it was Pamela – was still out to withhold any important information in my quest.

'Oliver Hope' ran the spidery handwriting. Birth date was given as July 7th 1912 (at least we have that, I thought triumphantly). But Oliver's stay at the school had been brief, indeed – from summer 1918 to Christmas 1919. And the parent or guardian column didn't contain my grand-mother's name at all. 'Mrs Willson' was written firmly under the heading at the top of the column. What on earth was I to make of this? Was Oliver really the son of a Mrs Willson? Where had he gone after leaving school at the tender age of seven? Phil had better have some answers.

*   *   *

'Mrs Willson?' Phil exclaimed on the phone from Wiltshire. 'My mother died last week. And she was Mrs Willson's best friend. If only you'd rung before . . . '

After condoling with Phil (his mother had died in her nineties), I asked if he could remember any of his mother's stories about Mrs Willson.

'Well yes, I can,' Phil said after a pause. 'It's a bit of a strange story, really. Your grandmother had a house built for Mrs Willson at Woodford [a neighbouring village] because she felt so guilty, so my mother heard.'

'Guilty?' What could have happened? I thought of young Oliver, removed from the village school and sent to Woodford to be with Mrs Willson and I couldn't work it out at all.

'Your grandmother's coachman was Mrs Willson's husband, John,' Phil said. 'One day your grandmother kept him waiting in the rain – on the box – and it was pouring down. John Willson caught pneumonia and died.'

I thought of the smart carriage restored by Phil and wondered, now the house was sold, if it was still in the stables at Wilsford Manor. I saw the stooped shoulders of John Willson as he sat waiting for my grandmother in the rain . . .

'But why did Mrs Willson take Oliver under her wing?' I asked, when the uncomfortable picture had faded. 'Did she want the child?'

Phil assured me that this wasn't the case at all. Children 'adopted' in those days would have been put in the care of a local woman from time to time – and Mrs Willson's name may well have appeared on the register because it wouldn't have been suitable for my grandmother's to have done so. In case she really was Oliver's mother, I thought, but refrained from saying so.

'The only other thing I remember Mrs Willson saying was that Oliver had turned out too rebellious to stay in the family,' Phil went on. 'They put him in the Royal Navy.'

But not at the age of seven, I silently objected. And the idea of Oliver being too rebellious was definitely interesting. What had he done to make his attendance at the school so short-lived? What had happened to ensure that Stephen, not known for his altruism, went on sending the lost brother pipes and tobacco to his ship? Most important, how did he really fit into the family?

*   *   *

By the time I went to see Fred and Eileen Newton, the only ones from the old days still to live at Wilsford, I was beginning to feel that I'd invented Oliver Hope – or, more likely, that my grandmother had. Wouldn't it be just like her to take the most 'magical' day in the year – so my astrological friends told me – the seventh day of the seventh month – and give it to this fantasy child as a birthday? Along with his name, the whole thing looked like something cooked up by J. M. Barrie in those far-off Peter Pan days. Wasn't Barrie a friend of Pamela's – he'd written a letter in a mock child's hand to young Bim. Maybe he and my grandmother made up Oliver Hope together. Of course, that didn't explain the school register – but maybe the entries in that and the weight chart were works of her imagination, too . . .

The final confirmation of my theory came when, on applying for a birth certificate for Oliver, I received a reply in the negative. In England, Scotland and Wales there had never been an Oliver Hope born on or even around that month or year.

I was lost. I had to get confirmation that Oliver Hope at least existed, or I'd doubt my grandmother's sanity, as well as my own.

'Oh yes, I knew Oliver,' Eileen said. She and her husband had been away and it was a huge relief to find the telephone answered in the cottage near the Manor where they had lived for close on forty years. Eileen's parents, Louis Ford and his wife, had lived and worked at the Manor in the days of Pamela and both her husbands – first Eddy, my grandfather, and then Edward Grey, Foreign Minister at the time of the Great War, whom Pamela married in 1922.

Louis had been coachman – perhaps due to the death of John Willson. He told me when I went down to Wilsford as a child that he and the other staff at the Manor had gone up to Stonehenge on Midsummer's Eve back in those long-gone Edwardian days, and had returned to the Manor and eaten up all the food in the house, they were so hungry. 'I had to go into Salisbury fast as I could,' Louis had said, 'to get breakfast for the guests at Wilsford.'

I was thinking of those stories of long-past opulence and of the surprising devotion Louis Ford retained to the end of their days to my grandmother and then to Stephen, with his mad parties and highly decorated existence, when Eileen dropped a hint about Oliver. 'Oliver married – a girl from Australia,'[2] Eileen said. 'But she went back there. No one here knows anything more.'

'And – did anyone say who Oliver might actually have been?' I asked. For the truth was turning out to be as elusive as ever: Eileen had been away from Wilsford, in Bath, during all the years she might really have got to know the child adopted by my grandmother.

'I've talked to a friend of mine – he's touching ninety but he lives just down the road,' Eileen's husband Fred put in. We were sitting at lunch in a Dorset pub and Fred had

---

2   There is no record of anyone named Oliver Hope marrying in the vicinity.

promised he'd try to find out all he could about Oliver before driving from Wilsford to see me and my partner, Tim. Tim had become as keen as I was by now on the quest for Oliver Hope, and we stared at Fred eagerly as the Lyme Bay plaice was set down before us. We knew now that Oliver was real, not invented. But there still wasn't an inkling of who his father and mother could actually be.

'Yes, my friend last saw Oliver Hope just after the last war, in Amesbury,' Fred said. 'And before the war, Oliver showed him round the *Lord Nelson* in Plymouth.'

'Did your friend say where he thinks Oliver came from?' I said.

'Your grandmother adopted four children in all,' came the surprising answer. 'Mary and Tossie and Roger – he had to ask your father what his real name was when he wanted to get married.'

'And Oliver?' I said faintly, when this strange set of circumstances had had a chance to sink in. 'What *was* his real name, Fred?'

'Oh, my friend down at Lake just said Oliver was the only one who was nobility,' Fred replied.

*   *   *

Later that evening, while still in Dorset, I rang the ancient friend of Fred and Eileen Ford. Could he tell me anything about Oliver Hope? What had he looked like, all those years ago? Did he resemble anyone in my family?

No, came the answer. Oliver had a round face and he was dark – but so, I commented, was Pamela. Surely, if she had – as I had been told by a family member – truly lived in a *ménage à trois* with my grandfather and Edward Grey, this dark-haired child could have been her son by Grey? Grey was childless and at that point still married to a wife with whom the marriage had never been consummated. It was possible to imagine the scandal of a late child (Stephen, the youngest, was five years old in the year of Oliver's birth) being hushed up and transformed into the adoption by Pamela of an orphan.

'Oliver was the son of a lord and an artist's model,' came the voice of the old man in Wiltshire. 'That's all we knew about him – he wasn't one of the children your grandmother had in and out of the Manor in those days. He was there.'

'Until he was sent away to the navy,' I said.

The old man chuckled. 'He was too rebellious to stay around, was Oliver.'

It was only when on my way back to London that I remembered a Wiltshire cousin and neighbour, Georgina, who had once shown me, in her farmhouse about fifteen miles east of Wilsford, the collection of privately printed books that had belonged to Pamela. Maybe there I would find the answer to the riddle of Oliver Hope.

Georgina was at home, and we settled down to look through the old letters and papers and books. It was a moving experience and what I found there began to convince me that Oliver was indeed a relative.

The white vellum notebook with Pamela's pencilled accounts of the bringing of the news of Bim's death, and subsequently of her encounters with her beloved son through the medium Gladys Leonard, made me think intensely of Bim.

What was he like, this film-star handsome young soldier-poet who had gone off to the trenches and lost his life there in September 1916? What had Bim's early years been? I knew his mother had loved him more than any of her children. I could hardly bear to look at the pencilled diagram in the vellum notebook which showed the exact spot in the trenches where Bim had fallen. There was an assurance from the General Command that the nineteen-year-old Bim had died instantly, without pain.

'Here is a rose from a fellow soldier, picked just before they went over the top,' Georgina said softly, handing me a flower black with the accretion of years. 'And here is the book Pamela had printed in his memory.'

It was when I saw the photographs of Bim as a very young man that I began to put two and two together. Dark and romantic, with rounded features, Bim could have been the father of Oliver Hope.

'But an artist's model?' queried Georgina. 'And wouldn't Bim have been barely fifteen years old at the time Oliver was conceived?'

The words of an elderly aunt came back to me as I sat on that rainy afternoon in Wiltshire, looking through the mementoes and photographs of the young man who had been heir to my grandfather Eddy's fortune and estates. 'Sex kittens,' my great-aunt Peggy had said on the occasion years before when I went to ask her more about my grand-mother Pamela. 'She couldn't stand the sight of the young ladies who used to come chasing down to Wilsford after her Bim, when he was still almost a child.'

The book fell open at the school report from Winchester, where Bim had gone as a boarder aged fourteen. Years ahead of his contemporaries both in intellect and physically, the headmaster had written. And a picture of Bim at the time confirms this: he was already a man. The 'artist's model' referred to by Fred's mate at the other end of Wilsford village must have been one of the girls so much disapproved of by my grandmother. I couldn't help smiling at the label 'sex kitten' applied in those years when the 'flapper' had just begun to appear on the scene.

There is no proof that Oliver Hope was the son of the eldest son of my grandfather. Pamela died in 1928, so my father must have had to organise the payment of the annuity I found out about in Greece. None of the other children 'adopted' by my grandmother received anything at all.

CHAPTER TWENTY-SIX

Glen: Taking Leave

SUMMER 1965

'Have you booked a sleeper?'

I'm in the tartan drawing-room, sitting at the desk where my mother used to sit before making her children write thank-you letters for the Christmas presents sent by friends of my parents who never came to stay but had fixed us all here in perpetuity: Elizabeth More O'Ferrall, wife of a rich racing man; Honey Harris, a member of the glamorous group of lesbians with their cropped dark hair who made their life in Paris around the Temple de l'Amitié on the Left Bank. Honey was my younger brother's godmother, so the severely wrapped brown-paper parcels in the Hall were more often for him than for me; but there were other offerings, scarves or soaps being as nothing to the books this infinitely subtle, acerbic and affectionate 'best friend' of my mother nevertheless managed to send me, in an almost secret way. (*Les Caves du Vatican* by André Gide, made its first appearance in my Christmas stocking when I was eleven years old; it was a French edition and I sensed it came from Honey; that I knew no French at that time seemed unimportant.)

'A sleeper?' I say into the telephone that sits on the

window seat by the walnut desk, now festooned with photographs of my brother's wife and their children. Why is it
that there is little more estranging than photographs of
relatives hardly known to one – strangers who have put
their mark, in smart leather frames, on the place one still
cannot stop oneself from calling home?

'Why?' I ask, knowing I sound stupid, if not rude, in my
inability to understand what my elder half-brother Colin
must mean by his insistence on my organising a sleeper to
London for myself and my son: we have just arrived here, no
more than two days ago, and I'm certain we never gave the
impression that we were expecting to pay a flying visit. Glen
is where I have come every holiday since I was eight years
old and had started school in London, when the war ended
and my parents went south to rescue the house in London
from bomb damage. My father loves his grandson and takes
him fishing on the loch as he once took me. What can be
meant by this demand from Colin?

'But you're arriving tomorrow,' I remind my brother,
pushing aside as I speak the picture of Colin in a Beatles
wig that has now taken pride of place on the writing table.
As I speak, I'm aware for the first time that I sound like an
owner, a hostess accustomed to welcome family and friends
to the house where she lives. And now, like a weight falling
on my shoulders, I begin to understand. My parents no
longer have any stake in Glen. They have decided to go
and live in Greece, and the entail, so often described and
regretted by my father, has ended with his move abroad.
Colin wants to be here alone or with his family – as laird, I
think, and almost burst out laughing, but the ludicrousness

of laughing at something we would once have found funny together, sobers me with as much force as the new, heavy thoughts which have come to me. Why did no one tell me that Glen had changed hands? How was I allowed, when informing my parents that I planned to go there, to continue in the certainty that all was as it had always been, when I could come and go as I wished? Did girls, under the laws of primogeniture, forfeit the right to learn the new set-up in the place they had considered theirs to visit when they pleased?

'I see,' I say into the receiver as my elbow nudges the expensively framed array of photos. I saw that I was no longer free to come and go. The last time I'd been here the little portrait gallery of family pics had not yet taken up residence on the desk. I think of hands moving the red- and blonde-haired children around, their positioning here is real; it is not intended as a joke.

*　　*　　*

Now the longest day of my life stutters towards the midway point: the lunch where we'll sit together around the long mahogany table which has been brought from the dining-room. (Colin is erecting false ceilings to cover the plaster fruit and foliage, and we must eat in the Hall.) I've seen Colin, but only briefly, as his time is taken up by new duties. He shouts up from the cellar to which he now holds the key. The voice, also handed down from father to son, underlines his ownership of the place – his impatience is to be expected.

'We haven't got a butler and I'm not one!' calls the maddened new laird of Glen; assembled with a squadron of nannies, his wife stands nervously in the freezing Hall.

At last, the new owner of the castle erected to hymn the business acumen of our great-grandfather appears dusty and distraught from the lower regions, a bottle of hock and a corkscrew in hand. I feel uncertain, as the ancient lift rattles up in the pantry: am I supposed to help bring out the dishes – collops, I see, with dumplings? Will this be the last simple meal, before a countess, a chocolate-box Gains-borough, arrives tonight for a long weekend? I know some-how that it will be the last time, too, that the children, the real-life models for the photos on the drawing-room writing desk, will be seated at a small table by the fireplace, over-looking the circular drive. Once the grand guests are here, the young will eat in the nursery, a long trek up the main stairs and out past the Doocot into the only part of the house untouched since Pamela's time: birds in bosky hedges on the Morris-papered walls, bright red yew berries hanging in clusters where they perch.

This lunch has an awkward atmosphere and I understand, as the name of the room I occupy is murmured by my hosts, that the Oak Room will be wanted later for the countess. So soon? I hear myself voice my surprise and dismay . . . but I haven't spoken at all . . . the only sound is the popping of the cork from a bottle of sweet German wine.

I leave the table as soon as possible. Now I know that Doug, who lives down in The Kennels where the dogs bark all day, has been told to drive us to Edinburgh. I can only count the hours: I know when the train goes; we must leave soon if we're to catch it.

There always has to be a reason, a crime, a misdemeanour that purports to explain a leave-taking as sudden as this. Of

course, at the time I don't know that we – my son and I –
must be branded as wrongdoers in an incontrovertible way,
nor that our identity is the true reason for the expulsion. I
stand at the foot of the main stairs as the little scene in the
drama plays out . . . Doug drives up in a Land Rover and
slides from his seat to stand in an attitude which refuses
responsibility for what has taken place. But he nods, as the
Head of the House is told the story – the grown-ups have
gone out to talk to him now . . . and one of the children is
crying . . .

This morning there have been shooting lessons in the
wood behind The Kennels on the back road to Glen. A bird –
I will never know if it was a pheasant or a crow – had been
'winged' and lay in pain until 'finished off' by one of the
children, a method taught by the gamekeeper to all would-
be young shots. I'm in the far end of the Hall by now, near
the vellum-bound albums. Through the Hall window, I hear
the conversation as it goes on. And the child is crying still .
. . adduced as proof of the necessity for our departure.

CHAPTER TWENTY-SEVEN

Harcourts

JULY 1982

A woman is standing in a shallow sea somewhere near Bantry Bay. It's where Aunt Anne likes to go to dig for cockles and clams, which will then be driven back to the simple cottage she has chosen to spend her summers in for some years past. I see the mud and lumps of shingle as they're prised from the shells with a short, ancient knife. Like the creatures inside, my aunt is following her deepest instinct – which is to protect herself from the rapacious hands of the outside world, to keep tight shut so that secrets can be guarded– and, above all, to resist talking about herself to anyone.

Anne had been rich – or was possibly still considered to be rich, by those who liked to exchange barbs and fragments of gossip in the art and literary world. Her philosopher husband, it was said, had married her for her money – although the couple's devotion to each other lasted many years. Then he left her for an American potter, pretty and wavy-haired, and he left children with my aunt, too, so she escaped to the cottage every summer. It was in a bare field outside the village of Schull (Anne hated gardens) and from there she went out daily to forage for food for her friends

134

and family. It was all free: mussels steamed in a battered cauldron picked up for nothing in a closing-down sale in Cork; baby crabs that crawled into her bucket and pinched our fingers as we stood round the table and helped Anne with her lengthy preparations for dinner; cockles and the samphire that grows along the cliffs by the sea.

'I don't see why he had to put that.' It's my mother talking. Like the rest of us, she has crammed into the low-ceilinged, in-need-of-a-coat-of-paint kitchen, and for once she looks quite flushed, put out even, a state her calm nature usually rejects.

'I suppose there's little anyone can do,' my aunt agrees, and she pushes a yellow and grey wisp of hair from her eyes, a gesture I always associate with the effort to make order, to establish a sense of harmony among hungry and possibly rebellious guests (on occasion the very freeness of the meals provided leaves people wanting more).

'I think you should write to the publisher of the book,' I say. 'If they've got your name wrong, they can change it when they reprint.'

I know, unlike anyone else at the table apart from my mother and Anne, just what is being discussed here. The reason lies in the odd sleeping arrangements my aunt has gone in for: upstairs there are three tiny bedrooms, with narrow single beds, and down here is a bathroom and an extra lavatory; this was considered a shocking luxury ten years ago, but insisted on by Anne's children and those guests who had been placed in the Donkey Room. (The Donkey Room was just outside the cottage and had to be walked out of by those in need of the bathroom, whether or

not rain fell or ice had formed on overhanging branches.)
While it was romantic, even flattering to be told on arrival
by my aunt that the Donkey Room had been selected for
one's accommodation, it did lead to some anxiety on the
long and dangerous journey (Anne was a frightening driver)
from Cork Airport.

On this occasion I had been spared the rigours of the
Donkey Room, and was placed upstairs in one of the thin
little bedrooms. I had woken in the middle of the night and
wanted to take a pee. There was no alternative to going
downstairs, and then past the sleeping form of my aunt,
who lay on a kind of truckle bed set up just by the entrance
to the bathroom and spare lavatory. 'I can't think why she
sleeps there,' my mother often said when the holiday was
over and we were back in London. That there was nowhere
else downstairs in the cottage to place a spare bed was never
discussed between us. The simplicity of Anne's life in Ireland
was beyond criticism: if she left only a dusty passage leading
to the bathroom for her sleeping quarters, it was a sign of
her desire to please those who had joined her in a life where
almost everything was free. Even the peat came for nothing,
as Paddy from two fields away was allowed to let his cow on
to Anne's stretch of grass in front of the cottage.

I knew what had annoyed Anne and my mother because
I'd seen Anne dozing on the put-up bed, and I'd seen the
book on the floor, where it must have slipped from her
hands when she finally succumbed, despite what must have
been terrible discomfort, to the urgent need for sleep. The
book was large and glossy – Anne would never in a thousand
years have bought it, though it could perhaps have been

sent from the publicity department of a publishing house – unlikely, as my aunt had never reviewed a book or for that matter worked in any paid capacity, preferring to live on whatever income was available, although she did drive a bus for a children's charity. No – I knew the book must have been sent by a friend. And why? Because my aunt and others we knew must surely be in its pages.

I had tiptoed past the bed and picked it up from the floor, visited the bathroom and absconded with the volume past the still sleeping body of my aunt. I had sat with it on my sleeping bag and the book had fallen open at once – the same page had been consulted several times. *The Diaries of Evelyn Waugh* – this was proclaimed on the jacket in gold against a background of dark brown and gold. The page looked innocently up at me as I stared and read again and again – until, eyes aching in the dim light, I found the hiding place for the cause of my mother and aunt's discontent. A footnote on that same page had Waugh explaining the identity of a couple who visited him in Capetown in the spring of 1941, on the long journey home from Turkey to Britain. The couple were my parents; my mother's maiden name was given as Elizabeth Harcourt-Powell.

To have been confronted by the Gorgon while reading the Greek myths would have probably been less overwhelming an experience than my confrontation with a lurking hyphen on that midnight research trip. Of all the pretentious (as Anne and my mother saw it) inventions open to the aspiring upper middle class, the adopting of a double-barrelled name was the worst. Those encountered at a party or art exhibition and introduced as bearers of two names, whether joined by a hyphen or not, were vilified later, their names 'forgotten', their achievements belittled to the point of extinction. Those with two bridged names were beyond the pale, as far as my mother and Anne were concerned. I admit I had never taken the trouble to wonder about or to enquire as to the source of this violent hatred of the elevated Smiths or Joneses. It just seemed, like various economies shared by the sisters, to be an eccentricity – they had a dislike for the 'genteel' which was sometimes exaggerated and marked their origins in an age more snobbish than our own.

But now, coming up against the discovery that I, too, came from a hyphenated family, had led me to decide I must find out more about this unexpected and unwanted connection. Who were the Harcourts – were they, I shuddered at the thought of finding out, actually Harcoors, like the impossibly grand French cousins of my half-brother Colin? Why had they been expunged so thoroughly from the family tree (not that there was one)? Neither Anne nor my mother could have tolerated the existence of any record of their past or their family; and now, beginning to see there really was something to conceal, I thought of them less as 'modern' women – egalitarian, left-wing, utterly devoid of any desire to discuss genealogies – and more as people with a desperate need for privacy and a desire, if possible, to bring about the total removal, except for their own children, of such a thing as the family. That the editor, novelist and letter-writer Evelyn Waugh, surely a highly educated and worldly man, had referred to my mother as a Harcourt-Powell suggested his own acceptance of the name. Was this use of a double barrel known to everyone when they met my mother or my aunt?

Of course not, came the silent answer as I had sat on with the heavy volume in my hand. No one had ever referred to them in this way . . . but then, I thought, they chose their friends precisely for their lack of worldliness. The painters and writers who came to visit would have had no interest in – and certainly no knowledge of – the significance of a Harcourt slipped in before the workaday Powell. Both Elizabeth and Anne had made sure they lived in a realm without a hyphen, and had clearly intended to continue that way – until now.

'It must have been in a reference book.' My mother has finished tugging at the resistant green hair extruding from the mussels, and sits back for a rest at the scrubbed pine table. I have been questioning her – cruel, I know – but while the sisters' mother was descended from the Priors, a family of Quakers and Catholics, and Mr Prior was a wealthy brewer of Trumans Beer, I still knew nothing of the Colonel's ancestry. (I didn't count the spurious Battenberg descent suggested by my half-brother.) I knew there were Harcourts somewhere, and now an innocent visit to a cottage in Ireland had shown their existence in print in the 1940s, I wanted to find out at last who they were. My mother and my aunt had been flushed out of their stance of total not-knowingness by the volume of Waugh's diaries and I let my imagination wander, as my mother remembered the huge journey that had to be undertaken, due to the closing of the Mediterranean in the war, in order to get from the Bosporus to the UK. I envisaged the stop-off in Capetown, the 'Commandos' they met there who were glamorous and brave, and who enjoyed the two days my mother and father spent with them. The young woman referred to by Waugh as Elizabeth Harcourt-Powell had been shy, but popular: her maiden name of no interest to those with a lack of enthusiasm for the double-barrelled. Only a snob of the calibre of Evelyn Waugh could have taken the trouble to include it in an unimportant footnote.

'But why would it have been in a reference book at all?' I insist.

'Lily Walsh's sons were called Harcourt and George,' my aunt suddenly – and surprisingly – puts in.

'You mean his first name was Harcourt – why?' I say, although it's obvious by now that Lily must have had a lover whose name was Harcourt, and this is where I would find him and solve the mystery. The Harcourts would show us, at last, where to look further – although, as so often with these searches, the result might be sad rather than exciting. It now seemed clear that the Colonel had been the second son of Lily Walsh and a Mr Harcourt – yet, as I pressed my questions, I saw that a kind of Joseph effect (as in Mary, Joseph and God) was taking place with the unknown supposed father, Mr Powell. It was as if the promise of a hyphen was enough to make monsters of us all; and the modestly born and possibly true parent of 'Harcourt' and 'George' had shrunk to a nobody overnight.

'Shall we go for one of the long walks this afternoon?' my aunt says.

'Yes,' my mother says, and they rise from the table, to place the plastic bucket containing the mussels and clams and cockles in the stained enamel sink.

'I'll come too,' I say, but I know as I speak that this isn't going to happen. Nothing will be said – for, as the shells are slowly opening in the running water from the (one) tap, my questioning has prised some unspoken knowledge from the sisters, and this can't be mentioned again, not on this trip anyway.

When I looked for the brown and gold hardback book of Evelyn Waugh's diaries, it was nowhere to be found; Anne had hidden it and it was never referred to again.

CHAPTER TWENTY-EIGHT

Glen: What Next?

APRIL 2009

'So what do they plan to do?' My mother and I are sitting in
the small house I have just exchanged for the flat ruined by
the property developer a few streets away in West London.
We're talking about various members of the family – my
mother loves to hear news about house moves or 'improve-
ments' undertaken by those who can still spend and borrow;
and today, after eating in the unseasonably hot small garden,
we've got on to Glen, always either dangerously exciting as a
topic, or hardly worth talking of at all. Of all her ninety-five
years my mother has spent forty out in Greece, where she
can still be found, having sold the house overlooking the sea,
known by me at least as The Last Redoubt, and bought a
village house not far inland. We're like cats, I decide, we go
out but we always come back again, to the place we know.
Perhaps we mind when the places change, the people who
own them imposing their own ideas on what had seemed so
familiar that it must last for ever.

I tell her that I've heard that Wilsford has become un-
recognisable since the death of my uncle Stephen Tennant
lost it to a wealthy buyer who has had it electronically
gated; it is no longer possible to walk down beside my

grandmother's grave, pause by the stone designed by Rex
Whistler and go on to the river and the Round House where
children used to play. But I'm aware that my mother has no
real interest in Wilsford. On the one occasion I went there
at the age of twelve, my father and I went together and
Louis Ford and his wife brought chicken and bread sauce,
the most incongruous of meals, to us as we sat in Stephen's
fantasy, a shell-studded room draped with Thai silk and
wallpapered in magenta flock. Once, that house had been
the past my father didn't like to revisit; now it looks like an
Indian restaurant, I couldn't help thinking – but my father
said nothing at all, other than to speak admiringly to Mrs
Ford of that other great English staple, broad beans, with
which our plates were plentifully heaped.

'Guests at Glen are encouraged to come down for breakfast with a notebook containing suggestions for a suitable
role the place could play in this day and age,' I tell my
mother. 'A conference is held in the Old Drawing-Room
where a placard is pinned to a board, proclaiming the subject
to be: "Glen: Ideas".'

'What?' comes the surprised reply from my mother. 'Can't
they just live in it . . . ?'

No, I tell her. The new 'owner', an eco-genius, mother of
the heir to Glen, has remarried recently, to a clever WASP
with plenty of plans for recreating a house and estate that
would have Sir Charles skipping out of his grave to applaud
the enterprise of the newly resident American. (Bella, the
reason for Henry's excited visit to my London flat all those
years ago, vanished to Canada several years back, her claim
on Glen gone and forgotten; her 'ownership' of Glen shown

to be nonsense.) 'They considered putting *trulli* in the Berks,' I say. 'You know, those little houses like beehives that you find in Southern Italy.'

'In the Berks? In the side of the hill?'

'Solar heating, a green way of life,' I go on teasing her. 'But I think that idea's been dropped . . . '

'But tell me about their new flat in London,' my mother says. The hills she once walked, the slow, long, cold years at Glen aren't as exciting to remember as innovations in the south; and she wants the details. Glen is too far away for her to feel anything when told about the changes envisaged there.

'Oh, they're in an all-glass flat,' I say – but I know my memory has taken me back to Glen: to the 'pearly' mornings Margot loved so much; to the Old Drawing-Room with Collina on her own small hill, erect in a white muslin dress and a sash, and Sir Charles's pointed features looking out from his portrait on the far side of the room. I can hear the songs, the jazz, the plaintive call of 'Creole Love Song', one of my mother's old collection of 78s, that was played again and again in that summer of '54 until the hypnotic effect made you too dizzy to stand.

'No curtains or blinds?' my mother says disbelievingly. She is more comfortable now, the flat is part of a new development in Bayswater and she knows the area well from a monotonous childhood in Hyde Park Gardens and Connaught Square. 'Don't they mind being stared at?'

'Not as far as I know. And they have a floating kitchen . . . '

So it goes on, but I'm not listening, even to myself. I see

my mother as she looks down the generations – for in the end she leaves the tales of the contemporary and is drawn back by my talk of the evenings at Glen, my efforts to remember the New Orleans song: 'Where you from? Where you from? Won'cha tell me 'fore I'm gone? . . . ' And soon the new inventions have disappeared and she is with me at Glen, too, by the log fire that was always needed in August . . . and my father standing over by the drinks tray, saying, 'We're getting low on Angostura bitters . . . '

I tell my mother of a recent visit to Glen by a young male member of the family. 'He's in love with the place,' I say.

'Oh, good.' It's the first time I've heard my mother so sarcastic. 'He can spend the rest of his life waiting for it to come to him.' And as I look across at her in surprise, the spell is broken and we're in my new cottage-house, on either side of the old table I've taken wherever I've moved, and Glen has vanished like an image on a screen. 'Glen is poison,' my mother says. And we both fall silent, as our thoughts are crowded by the cousins and uncles, the claimants and pretenders who saw Colin disappear to the Caribbean and dogged my father, as he grew old, with demands for part of the estate – or for Wilsford, where Stephen died intestate. They all wanted Glen, and my mother must have put up with the threats and promises they offered in return for a life there.

'Yes, I suppose so,' I say.

CHAPTER TWENTY-NINE

February 10th 2005

I'm sitting with a cup of coffee in my flat in West London when the mail clatters into the hall through a letter box newly installed by a property developer who has taken over the building with plans to wreck any idea of peace or silence in this normally agreeable crescent. I go out through an inner front door – this already splashed with paint from a careless decorator's brush – and stand for a moment looking down at the tangle of BT bills, catalogues of children's clothes (pointless for me and certainly not wanted by the developer), and I see there is just one letter, a 'real' letter, rare in the age of e-mail and pizza promotions. I retrieve the oblomg envelope, slitting the edge with my thumb as I straighten up. Already – and I don't know why – my hackles are rising: I feel the presence of an intruder in the bow-windowed, unassuming ground-floor flat I have occupied for several years now. Partly, perhaps, because my name is 'wrong', typed at the heading of the letter: Lady Emma Tennant (which is my sister-in-law's name). It is addressed c/o my publisher, Jonathan Cape.

Dear Madam – Re Robert Brown, born January 5th 1955, illegitimate child of Princess Margaret [runs the opening line and, just beneath this:] I have reason to

146

believe that I may be the illegitimate child of Princess Margaret. [My eye travels down to the bullet points towards the bottom of the page.] No 2. Your half-brother Lord Glenconner was a key figure. You may or may not be aware I wrote to your brother some time ago in the hope he may have been able to help directly, respond or intercede privately. He did not reply, which was not entirely unexpected.

*   *   *

Apart from the information that a person he refers to as his mother Cynthia Werner had been a model and had worked at Hardy Amies and Harrods as a 'floor model' – 'I believe Cynthia was photographed by Baron' – Robert Brown concentrates on the various steps he has taken to establish his identity as Princess Margaret's son. These include application to the Courts for judicial review of the intransigence of the Constitutional Department; a resolution to petition Parliament to consider and determine the rights of illegitimates; and application to the High Court for confirmation that Farrers were the executing solicitors in respect of HM the Queen Mother's will.

'The will,' Robert Brown goes on, 'was kept closed on the application to the High Court. I am surmising that the order would not have been given except, for example, to protect the interests of say an illegitimate child provided for within the will . . . '

And so on. Mr Brown hopes that 'bringing the matter into the public domain may force a response, or bring forth evidence to support it . . . '

By the time I've scanned this, uncertain of my true response, the coffee has grown cold in the kitchen. By a jam jar of wilting snowdrops I stand at the top of the rickety steps which lead down to the basement, my head full of pictures, some old and black-and-white – the floor model as she tours the stifling, carpeted showroom at Harrods; others bright technicolour, where the purple mountains of Glen sweep down to the narrow road that leads up to the loch. Can it be – could it be true? Surely, the comments of the judiciary are bound to be scathing – if they go to the trouble of making any judgment at all. This pretender can be waved away like a fly. 'I have not sought to determine paternity, although based on the press reports of the day there would be some obvious candidates, including . . . '

It's hard to walk down the wooden steps to the floor below while holding a mug in one hand and a document in the other. I let the letter go, so it drifts down and ends on the radiator by the door out into the area. I reach the lower level and carry the mug to the sink, to wash out the sediment that has gathered inside. A black stream oozes into the waste and blocks the plughole so I have to turn on the taps hard.

'Oh, the man who's trying to open the royal wills.' A friend who is also a friend of the lawyer who has taken on this strange petition shrugs invisibly as I stand in my kitchen talking to him on the phone. 'It's quite wrong that the public should be refused access to the royal wills, of course,' my friend says. 'In the UK everyone has a right to obtain access to a will. I'm not surprised your Mr Brown is indignant. He probably has no chance of being believed when he says who he thinks he is – but he has a right to see the Queen Mother's will or Princess Margaret's.'

'God I hope not,' I say – meaning I hope there will never be proof to back his obsessive solution to his ancestry.

A dreamer . . . but then, after the regulation period of slowly passing time, when the case came up, a decision was reached in favour of Mr Brown. The wills would be opened, after all. The judge, predictably, was scathing on the subject of the claim of identity as illegitimate son of Princess Margaret – but the wills could be opened. This has not happened yet: there has been no date given for the final evidence sought by Mr Brown. There was a leader in the *Guardian*, praising his endeavours: Robert Brown, accountant of Jersey, had gained the right to appeal.

CHAPTER THIRTY

October 18th 2007

Two and a half years have passed, and I'm out in Greece. It's tricky getting a newspaper in this village on the west coast of Corfu, and I almost didn't bother to ask a friend staying in the house if he could bring one back with him from a planned visit to the town. 'I bet they'll only have the *Telegraph*,' I call after him as he goes, 'if so, don't bother . . . '

There are times when one knows a play is about to be enacted: the action has been sketched out and the players are in place. After an unusually short visit to the arcades and coffee shops of Corfu, my friend returns waving a newspaper. 'Just what you predicted', he says, throwing it down on the sofa. 'Nothing in it – expensive, too.'

His voice goes on, complaining that it's only the Royal Family this paper is interested in and why did he bother to buy one? As he speaks two more people come in, and then a third, a close friend who has heard me in the past on the subject of the strange letter from Robert Brown. All three stop dead as they reach the back of the plump, blue-and-white-striped sofa, where the newspaper lies photo up.

There, instantly identified in the small black-and-white picture, is a middle-aged man with a bald, domed head. Those who had known my father asked what the photo was doing there, why it was captioned 'Robert Brown appeals'?

This was the way the past enacted its rituals in a Greek village house a thousand miles from the lochs and valleys of Glen. This was a reminder, however unexpected, of the power of possibility over fact.

'But I can't understand why – if Princess Margaret was his mother, after all – ' my friend who knew my father says as the strange story comes out – 'wouldn't it be getting obvious . . . when was it again?'

'The summer of 1954,' I reply. But all I see are the fat game birds as they are carried round the table on the first evening of the royal visit. And I see a woman's back, over-padded with flesh, pulling forward as serving spoons and forks lift the thighs and breasts of the grouse and lower them on to plates.

'I don't know,' I say when pressed for theories, facts, information. I sound like my mother: 'I really don't know,' I say.

The End

March 2007

My elder half-brother is counting his emeralds and rubies on the terrace of his newly completed Taj Mahal on the Pitons in St Lucia when I arrive for a visit, not having seen him for years. Colin goes in and fetches a sheet of paper from his elegant four-postered bedroom. As light fades over the sea below, I try to make out the meaning of the family tree he has sketched there. And I see – but cannot believe – the connection we apparently share, in this family where no one is what they seem and no secret remains unshared . . .

Harcourts abound in Colin's family tree. In mine, as portrayed by him, there is only one, but it is from him that we are both descended. I can't help wondering if my father knew he was connected twice to the same family – through Colin's mother respectably, and through Lily Walsh and her son 'Colonel George', my mother's father, in the concealed fashion that was the norm in Edwardian society when illegitimate children were involved.

'Mrs Keppel was kind to Lily,' I say, as a dish of the Caribbean vegetable christophine appears and my brother takes a tiny portion. He has given up eating in the evening, he says, as he doesn't want to miss his swim.

The last I see of my doubly related brother is his back in a white bathrobe, as he goes down the unmade road to the sea.